Mammals

Mammals

Anatomy • Behaviour • Habitat

Contents

PRIMITIVE MAMMALS 54

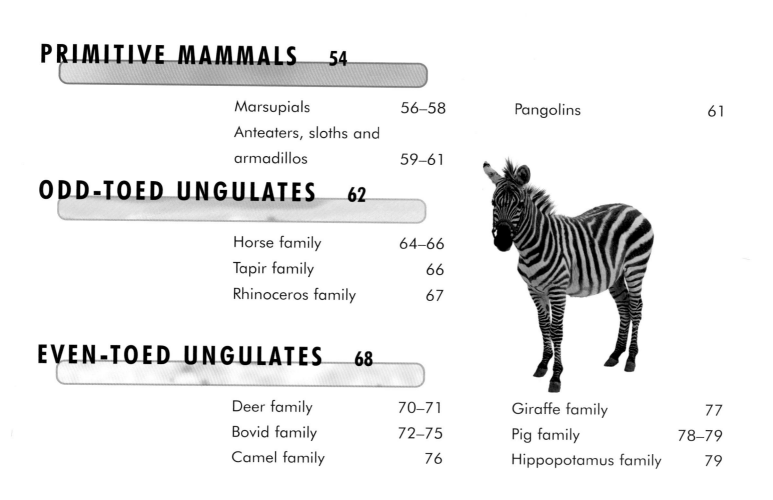

ODD-TOED UNGULATES 62

EVEN-TOED UNGULATES 68

MAMMALS WITH TRUNKS 80

MARINE MAMMALS 86

APPENDIX 94

Introduction

Probably the best-known category of our animal kingdom is that of the mammals, not least because they include human beings themselves. Many mammals are to be found in our immediate environment. We keep some of them as working animals (the horse) or as protectors (the dog), whilst others provide us with high-quality food (beef).

All mammals have a closed, efficient blood circulatory system and a heart, each equipped with two chambers and two antechambers. They breathe with lungs and have a nervous system which divides into two branches. The skull is separated from the spinal column. There are always seven neck vertebrae, which vary in size depending on the animal; they are partly fused together in a few animals.

Highly evolved mammals have well-developed sensory organs and a powerful brain. As they are warm-blooded, they are relatively unaffected by changes in temperature. Most mammals are covered in hairs or bristles, and scales or spines.

Mammals reproduce by fertilisation of the female by the male. Females give birth to live offspring that have developed in the womb. The young are then nourished by their mother's milk, which they suck from mammary glands or teats. Marsupials are an exception to this, as they give birth to relatively undeveloped young. Further development of the young takes place in the mother's pouch. Other exceptions are the monotremes or egg-layers – echidnas (spiny anteaters) and platypuses. These animals lay eggs, but after hatching the young are also suckled in just the same way as other mammals.

Platypuses live in various Australian and Tasmanian rivers. A distinctive feature of these mammals is the venom-producing spur of the male.

Unlike most mammals, the echidna, which also lives in Australia, has evolved with no teeth. Teeth have been replaced by hard pads. Their diet consists of worms, insects, ants and termites, which they lick up with their tongue from the ground.

The evolution of mammals began about 220 million years ago in the Upper Triassic. At first, they only played a minor role, because at that time reptiles dominated the animal kingdom, and in particular the dinosaurs. Simple species of mammals, which evolved from reptiles, are the egg-layers previously mentioned. Other early mammals were burrowing or shrew-like animals, which fed on small animals and plants.

With the extinction of the dinosaurs 65 million years ago, the appearance of the Earth changed. The species-rich evolution of the mammals began, until it reached the peak of its diversity about 15 million years ago. When climatic conditions deteriorated in the following years and many tropical rainforests were lost, the number of species dramatically declined. With temporary Ice Ages occurring during the Pleistocene period 2 million years ago, new and often large mammals such as mammoths, giant deer or woolly rhinos evolved. These animals have died out completely in the last 12,000 years.

Other mammals further evolved depending on their habitat. They developed long, slender legs to move fast in the savanna or prairie, and flexible limbs with long fingers to grip, in order to climb trees.

The structure of their teeth varies depending on the type of food they eat. However, in the course of their life, all mammals acquire first the milk teeth and later the adult teeth.

The bat family

The bats and flying foxes sub-classifications are members of the bat family. Bats are the only mammals whose forelimbs evolved as proper wings.

Their body is squat with a short neck and an elongated head. The hands are greatly enlarged. The fingers, between which the flying membranes are located, are elongated. Only the thumb has a claw, which the bat uses to climb or grip firmly.

The flying membranes, which have a span of 20–60 cm, are spread out like an umbrella so that they flutter when the bat flies. When they are at rest, bats hang from the edges of walls or beams by the claws of their hind legs. The whole body, including the head, hangs down in this way; at the same time, the wings lie close to the body. Bats use the tail skin to steer when they fly. They are skilful fliers, but are very clumsy on the ground. They come out at dusk to hunt mainly beetles and moths; this enables bats to benefit from their acutely pronounced senses, because even in complete darkness, they can detect the smallest obstacles.

The females of this animal family usually give birth to a single offspring, which they carry around with them constantly during the first months of its life. Our native species hibernate during the winter. For this purpose, they look for a cave, an attic or a vaulted cellar.

Bats

Bats are small mammals that can fly. They owe their ability to fly to a delicate flying membrane, which spans across the whole body.

At the side of a bat's body – which can live up to 16 years – the flying membrane is attached, supported by the arm. It is extended by the upper and lower legs, the upper arms and forearms, as well as by the greatly elongated

Bat (Horseshoe)

Range:
worldwide except in the polar regions

Habitat:
tropical, sub-tropical and temperate climates

Bats are the only mammals that can fly properly. The Horseshoe Bat belongs to a family of about 70 species. To navigate, it sends ultrasonic waves through its nose.

metacarpals and phalanges (finger bones). The smaller tail membrane is supported by the back legs and tail.

Bats are covered in mouse-grey hairs and have striking ears next to their head the so-called 'bat ears'.

Bats have poor sight, and therefore they have excellent hearing to compensate. They let out a very high-pitched shriek at 170 cycles a second, which we cannot hear, because the frequency lies in the range of ultrasound.

When these sound waves bounce off their prey or any obstacles, they come back as an echo. The bats hear the echo, which allows them to get their bearings. The outgrowths on the nose of some species of bat are also probably used to locate the echo. Through this so-called echolocation, it is possible for bats to fly about in caves or forests in pitch black, without bumping into anything. They catch their prey in the same way (see illustration, page 12).

They can catch and grip their prey with the sharp claws attached to their feet, which are not enclosed in the flying membrane. These feet are ill-suited to walking. At best, bats can only hobble across the ground on them.

Bat

thumb

flying membrane

However, bats are expert at climbing up and down trees and walls. When they sleep, they hang by their back legs, with their head facing downwards. If they want to fly, they drop down and at the same time unfold their flying membrane.

The bat starts hibernating in October. For this purpose, it looks for a hiding-place in a frost-protected and damp, but cool, cellar or tunnel, where it remains until the beginning of March. Some species of bat fly several hundred kilometres to reach their winter quarters, whilst others stay in the vicinity.

Large groups are almost always to be found together in their winter quarters. In preparation for hibernation, bats lower their body temperature and slow down their metabolism to the minimum. This

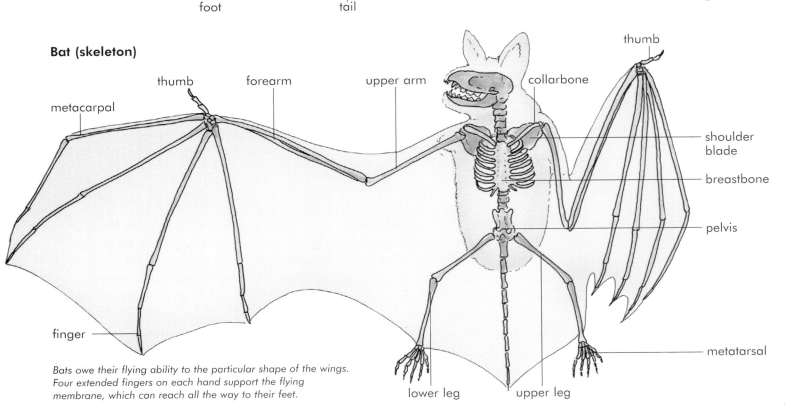

sharp teeth

cone-shaped ears

leg

foot

tail

is the only way that their energy reserves will last over the winter, which they have built up by feeding during the summer. Every disturbance during winter hibernation, when, for example, people enter the cave to watch the bats, means that they use up additional energy to heat up their body and regulate their metabolism. Therefore, their energy reserves can be spent prematurely. Then the bat will starve before spring comes and the first insects fly again. A common species is the **Brown Long-Eared Bat**. It is found throughout Europe with the exception of northern countries lying above latitude 60°. It lives near residential housing, in gardens, in hollow trees or in attics.

The long-eared bat grows to only about 8.4 cm long, of which the tail accounts for 4 cm. The wing span

Bat (skeleton)

thumb

forearm

upper arm

collarbone

thumb

metacarpal

shoulder blade

breastbone

pelvis

finger

metatarsal

lower leg

upper leg

Bats owe their flying ability to the particular shape of the wings. Four extended fingers on each hand support the flying membrane, which can reach all the way to their feet.

measures 24 cm. The ears are 3.3 cm long, which is disproportionate compared to the rest of the body. During flight, the huge ears, which have numerous horizontal folds, are arched outwards, so that the tips of the ear are set upright pointing forwards. When the bat hangs down and goes to sleep, it tucks its ears under its wings.

The bat's face is covered in long hair, and whitish whiskers hang down from around its lips. The long coat is mostly grey-brown and a little darker in young bats.

The so-called **Mouse-Eared Bat** is 13 cm long (5 cm of which constitutes the length of the tail) and is the largest bat in central Europe. These bats have a wingspan of 37 cm. The back is reddish brown, and the underbelly is light in colour. During the day, this species is mainly found in quiet hiding places such as attics, churches or castles. Mouse-eared bats are widespread and can also still be found in mountain ranges of up to 1,200 m in height. In common with many species, they search for a place in a cave or a vault in winter.

The **Noctule**, which is found throughout Europe, is 11 cm long, 4 cm of which constitutes the length of the tail. They have a wingspan of 37 cm, and live in woodpecker holes and tree crevices. You can recognize their dens by the greasy and smelly entrance. This bat often leaves its hideout to hunt even before it gets dark.

Vampire Bats are feared by people. They live in the jungles of Central and South America. These 8 cm-long bats have large, prominent ears and no

Vampire bat
Range: **Central and South America**
Habitat: **forest**

tail. They feed exclusively on blood, by biting with their teeth and making deep wounds mostly in the skin of deer and horses. They lick up the blood that trickles out. This does not often cause their victims any pain, because the vampire bat's teeth are extremely thin and sharp.

But not all bats belonging to this group are bloodsuckers. Many feed simply on insects, and some even eat fruits too.

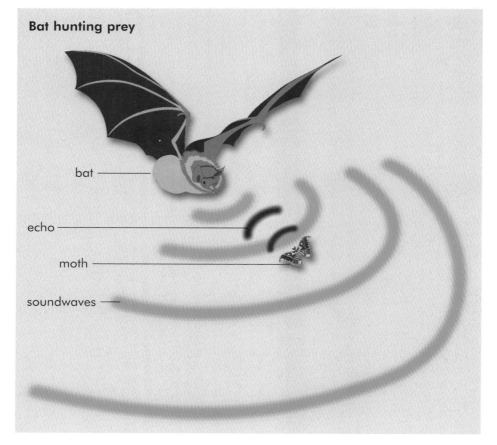

Bat hunting prey

bat

echo

moth

soundwaves

Bats are night hunters and can detect their prey with great skill even in darkness. To this end, when they are flying they send out calls in the ultrasonic range, which we cannot hear. When these sound waves encounter an obstacle, their large ears receive the returning echo. The time between sending out and receiving the sound waves is shorter or longer, depending on how far away their prey is located. Therefore, bats know exactly where they are, locate the prey precisely and hunt it down in flight.

Flying foxes

Flying fox Range: **Africa, Australia and South Asia**
Habitat: **forest and scrubland**

Flying foxes or fruit bats are members of the bat family, with about 200 species found throughout Australia, Africa and South Asia.

Flying foxes and bats do have a similar build, because flying foxes also have flying membranes between their limbs. However, the head has a more dog-like or fox-like appearance, which is also where the name, flying fox, came from. On average, flying foxes are considerably larger than bats, but there are a few smaller species. The wingspan of a flying fox ranges between 24 cm and 180 cm, depending on the species.

During the day, flying foxes are to be found in the trees of dark and dense forests and more rarely in caves. Here, they often hang from the branches in large groups and sleep, whilst shrouding their head and body in their wings.

Like every member of the bat family, flying foxes become active at night. Their large eyes help them to see well at dusk. However, unlike bats, they find their food –which consists of ripe fruits –not with the help of sound waves, but with their very keen nose. They head for a tree and hang on to the branches with their hind feet and the strong claw attached to their thumbs. Some species also use a second claw for this purpose. They move along in the trees using their feet and claws.

Sometimes flying foxes also invade banana and mango plantations, where they have a good time, to the displeasure of the farmers. Smaller species eat flower nectar and pollen, and even petals. Other species, which are referred to as lesser **Long-Tongued Fruit Bats**, have a particularly long tongue, which they can dip into the calyx of flowers to extract the nectar and pollen. As a result, many pollinate the flowers at the same time. All flying foxes of this kind are vegetarians.

When flying foxes can no longer find enough food in a forest, they usually migrate. In the process, they can cover long distances and also fly across the sea to reach a neighbouring island.

Once a year, the female gives birth to one or two offspring. The young hang onto their mother's breast and she carries them around with her all the time. Therefore, unlike bats, the young do not stay behind when the mother goes in search of food.

The largest species of flying fox is the **Kalong** or the **Greater Flying Fox**. It grows up to 1.50 m long and lives on Java and Sumatra. The colour of its back and flying membrane is brown-black, whilst the belly, neck and head are somewhat more reddish. It loves figs and mangoes and therefore causes considerable damage to many fruit plantations when they are invaded by hundreds, even thousands, of Kalongs.

Primates

Monkeys, apes, prosimians and humans belong to the primate order of mammals. It comprises about 400 species, which are very different from each other.

APES AND MONKEYS

Apes and monkeys can be divided into two large sub-orders: **Old World Monkeys** or **Catarrhine Monkeys** and **New World Monkeys** or **Platyrrhine Monkeys**. Members of the **Old World Monkey** group include the gibbon, the apes and the long-tailed monkey families. They can only be found in the eastern hemisphere. As their nostrils lie very close together, they are also known as **Hook-Nosed Monkeys**.

New World Monkeys include howler monkeys, capuchins and marmosets. They live in the tropical jungles of South and Central America. As their nostrils are set wide apart, they are also known as **Flat-Nosed Monkeys**.

PROSIMIANS

Prosimians also have hands and feet that grip, with which they can move expertly through the trees. Their faces are mostly elongated and fox-like. They mainly live in trees in Africa and Asia.

Apes and monkeys

In the past, apes and monkeys could be found over a much larger area of the world. Today, their habitat is confined to warm regions, because monkeys are very sensitive to cold, except for a few baboon species. Each continent has its characteristic species, but there is only one remaining species in Europe.

Monkeys mainly live in forests and are well-adapted to a life clambering amongst the trees. However, apes and baboons are not so mobile. Other species of monkey can be seen jumping briskly from tree to tree, whilst the tail and back legs are used to manoeuvre through the canopy. As the tail is a fifth hand, which can be used to grip, many species can hang from a branch and swing, or easily grab their food. Monkeys live on leaves and fruits from the trees, but also on roots and tubers. Sometimes, they eat eggs and young birds as well. Monkeys are agile when it comes to climbing, but they often appear ungraceful and awkward when they walk on the ground. For example, gibbons walk upright and try to keep their balance by stretching their arms out. Other species support themselves with

Capuchin monkey
Range: **Central and South America**
Habitat: **forests**

their hands, so that they can then swing forwards with their body and back legs.

Monkeys are very social animals. Most live in larger communities, where the oldest or strongest male assumes control and responsibility for the safety of the troop.

Female monkeys bear a single infant at a time, which clings to the mother following birth. She carries it around with her constantly, enabling it to suckle.

Monkeys have a large brain and are very quick to learn. Using their animated facial expressions and different sounds they are able to communicate with each other well.

The gibbon, the ape and the long-tailed monkey families belong to the **Old World Monkey** or hooked-nosed monkey group. Similarly, howler monkeys, capuchins and marmosets belong to the **New World Monkey** or flat-nosed monkey group.

Chimpanzee

Chimpanzees are probably the most popular apes. These intelligent animals live in Central and West Africa in the rainforests, and on savannas with tree cover. They grow up to 1.75 m tall and have a strong, stocky body. The males are a little larger than the females. Their slender arms are a little longer than their legs, and they have opposable thumbs, which means that the thumbs can touch the other digits.

A chimpanzee's coat is very dark brown to black, whilst the face is a lighter colour; their lips are highly mobile. Chimpanzees live in troops and can communicate with each other by facial expression and a variety of sounds. As they are good climbers, they forage for fruits, leaves, nuts and eggs in trees. They also eat tree bark and insects. Chimpanzees use small sticks to 'fish' ants or termites out of their nests. Chimpanzees use stones to break open coconuts. They use

Lowland gorilla
Range: **Africa**
Habitat: **tropical rainforests**

Mandrill
Range: **Gabon and Cameroon**
Habitat: **forests**

Long-tailed monkeys
Range: **Africa**
Habitat: **steppe and savanna**

Spider monkey
Range: **South America**
Habitat: **tropical forests**

Young chimpanzee
Range: **Africa**
Habitat: **savanna with trees, rainforest**

Rhesus monkey
Range: **India**
Habitat: **forest bordering the banks of the River Ganges**

tufts of grass to clean their fingers, which are often sticky, and their coat. Most of the time chimpanzees walk on the ground, where they move along on all fours. But they walk upright, if they are holding food in their hands. Chimpanzees forage for their staple diet during the day, in the course of which they cover up to several kilometres. They also kill small antelopes,

bush pigs and small monkeys in the process. Several chimpanzees join forces for the hunt and ambush the prey.

Chimpanzees mainly live in an informal order in troops of up to 100 animals. The hierarchy is not as strict as it is with gibbons. There are various ranks within the community, which are determined according to strength and wisdom. There are also individual groups of males that continually engage in more minor power struggles. These tussles become very noisy and involve all kinds of gestures and

loud screaming. It is less likely to result in a full-blown fight.

When several monkey family members meet, loud screaming

Chimpanzee (skeleton)

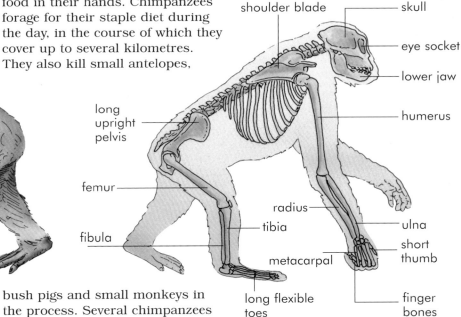

- shoulder blade
- skull
- eye socket
- lower jaw
- long upright pelvis
- humerus
- femur
- radius
- fibula
- tibia
- ulna
- short thumb
- metacarpal
- long flexible toes
- finger bones

and plenty of embracing starts up amongst the relatives. In addition, chimpanzees all sit together and begin grooming each other socially. Whilst doing so, they remove lice and fleas from each other and therefore demonstrate their common bond.

The females rise in rank the older they become and the more infants they bear, and mostly remain with other females and their infants. Young chimpanzees

learn from their mothers how to survive in the wild. They climb, hunt and play a lot, whilst finding out everything they need to know to survive as an adult chimpanzee.

Chimpanzees spend the night in trees, building nests made of twigs they interweave. Young chimps under three years of age sleep with the females.

The females are ready to conceive at fixed times and mate with all the males of the group. After a gestation period of about 230 days, usually a single infant is born, and sometimes two. The infant stays close to its mother over the next few years.

Chimpanzee (anatomy)

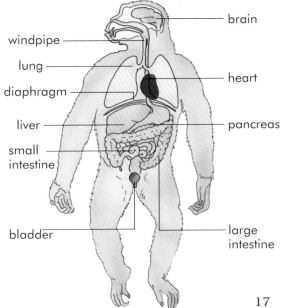

- brain
- windpipe
- lung
- diaphragm
- heart
- liver
- pancreas
- small intestine
- bladder
- large intestine

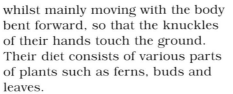

Gorilla

The gorilla is the largest of the apes. The males grow to over two metres tall and weigh up to 250 kg. However, the females are considerably smaller. **Lowland Gorillas** live in the tropical rainforests of Africa. **Mountain Gorillas** live in the mountain rainforests of Uganda, Rwanda and Congo.

In the past, gorillas were portrayed in numerous films and stories as enormous monsters. With their huge body covered in black, shaggy hair, and their broad shoulders, gorillas appear very

Gorilla
Range: **Africa**
Habitat: **rainforest**

threatening and dangerous. But they are amongst the most gentle and most peaceful of apes.

Gorillas live in family groups, which consist of five to eight females and their offspring. A so-called silverback presides over them; that is to say, a larger male gorilla with a silver-grey back (which he acquires from the age of ten). When a leader dies, the young gorillas fight amongst themselves to be his successor.

Gorillas roam their territory together as they forage for food,

whilst mainly moving with the body bent forward, so that the knuckles of their hands touch the ground. Their diet consists of various parts of plants such as ferns, buds and leaves.

The females and their young also climb up trees to pick fruits. The heavyweight males are incapable of doing this. They go looking for their staple diet in the morning and in the afternoon. In between, they sleep in a rapidly built nest during the day, and then they start foraging again. Gorillas do not need to drink extra water, as the plants and berries they eat contain plenty.

During the night, they rest in nests built from twigs and leaves. For the first few years, young gorillas remain with their mothers overnight.

The mating of the gorilla can take place at any time of year. After a gestation period of about nine months, a single infant is born. For the first few months, the infant is carried around by the mother, as it clings onto her fur. Only after three months can it sit upright, and two months later it can walk and climb. Overall, the infant is suckled by its mother for almost a year and a half, and furthermore continues to remain with its mother until it is three years old.

When neighbouring groups encounter each other, it sometimes results in conflicts. However, rivals are repelled with a threatening gesture as the males rise up and beat their chest. At the same time, they bark out powerful hoots and roars, rip tufts of grass from the ground as a sign of their overwhelming strength and throw it around. Large fights don't usually occur.

Gorillas can live up to 50 years of age. In the UK, gorillas are kept in almost every zoo and also reproduce there.

Orang-utan

The orang utan (meaning 'person of the forest' in the Malay language) is native to the rainforests of Sumatra and Borneo. It is the second-largest species of primate. Unlike gorillas, which live on the ground, orang utans are almost always to be found in the treetops.

Male orang utans grow up to 1.75 m tall and weigh about 75 kg. Their build resembles that of humans, because the upper body is not compressed at the sides, as in the case of other mammals; but they have pronounced broad shoulders instead, like those of humans. Young orang utans are the most similar to humans, as far as the overall picture is concerned. As they grow older, their forehead recedes further and their mouth curves like a snout. Substantial bulges develop above the eyes.

Males develop broad skin flaps on both sides of the face – the so-called 'flanges'. Their teeth are structured in a similar way to those of humans, but are much more powerful. The animal has a strong bite and can also break into fruits with solid shells.

The orang utan's coat is reddish-brown, long and shaggy. In male orang utans, the face is hairless except for the beard.

Orang utans rarely come down to the ground, because they find their food in the trees: leaves, fruits and shoots. They drink water from holes in branches and trees, which are constantly filling up as it rains nearly every day. Their feet and

Young orang-utan
Range: **Borneo and Sumatra**
Habitat: **rainforest**

hands are equally good gripping tools: the toes and fingers are long and flexible. Like the thumbs next to their fingers, they have opposable big toes that can touch the other toes. However, to climb orang utans mainly use their arms, with which they can effortlessly move hand over hand, with a span of over two metres, from branch to branch.

Orang utans are clumsier on the ground, because their legs are less well developed. Their feet, which they use to grasp, are curved a little inwards and therefore they have an awkward-looking gait. They use their arms as supports. Particularly when they have to walk quickly, orang utans move forwards whilst drawing up their arms and swinging through with their body and bent legs.

Orang utans live alone or in pairs together with their young. During the night, they sleep in the forks of branches. Sometimes, they even cover themselves with various parts of plants. They probably look for a new place to sleep every night. They make it clear where the borders of their territory lie by engaging in loud bellowing.

About every two years, the female orang utan – which is smaller than the male – gives birth to a single infant, after a gestation period of almost nine months. She cares for and looks after her offspring for several years. It has been observed that the offspring are suckled for up to six years in captivity.

The orang utan is an endangered species. Their numbers have dramatically declined, due to a low birth rate and human activities. Strict rules to protect orang utans should save this animal from extinction.

Baboon

The baboon is a species that belongs to the long-tailed monkey family. There are five different subspecies of baboon, which live in the savannas and steppes of Africa and Saudi Arabia.

The length of a hamadryas baboon's body is up to 95 cm. The coat is a brownish colour. The males are almost double the height of the females and have a thick mane on their chest and shoulders and on both sides of the head. The pads of skin on their protruding buttocks are particularly striking, which turn to red in the females especially during the mating season. They have a dog-like snout and the canine teeth are relatively long.

Baboons are social ground-dwellers that live together in family troops with an older male as the leader. They use an extensive range of gestures and sounds to communicate with each other.

During the day, they forage together for food, which consists of plants, insects and other small animals. At night, baboons rest in rock crevices or trees, where they also seek refuge from their greatest enemy, the leopard.

After mating, a gestation period of about 170 days follows, after which a female baboon gives birth to a single infant, and sometimes two, between May and July. At first, the infant clings to its mother's coat for several weeks and is later carried on her back.

Baboon
Range: **Saudi Arabia and Africa**
Habitat: **savannas and steppes**

Prosimians

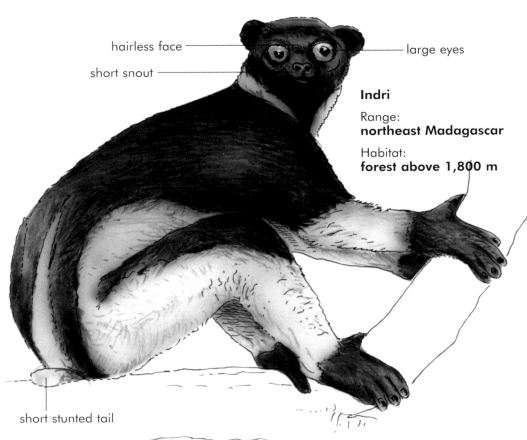

hairless face ——

short snout ——

—— large eyes

Indri

Range:
northeast Madagascar

Habitat:
forest above 1,800 m

short stunted tail

Prosimians bear little resemblance to monkeys. Their tail is often longer than their entire body, but in many species it is completely stunted. Individual species are between a few centimetres and almost one metre tall.

Prosimians include the **Aye-Aye**, the **Loris** and the **Lemurs** (Makis, Indri family).

Indri and aye-aye

The indri family, which belongs to the prosimians, consists of three groups, namely **Sifakas**, **Woolly Lemurs** and the single **Indri**. They are native to the forests of Madagascar.

White sifaka (prosimian)
Range: **Madagascar**
Habitat: **dry forest and rainforest**

With a body length of 70 cm, the indri is the largest of them all. It has a very short tail, which sets it apart from the other groups. Both the sifaka and the indri have very loud voices, with their howling and wailing sounds.

The indri lives on the ground as well as in the trees. During the day, it forages for leaves, fruits and shoots.

Indris mate at the beginning of the year and after a gestation period of about five weeks, the female gives birth to a single infant.

One strange nocturnal animal is the aye-aye. As the name would suggest, it has very long fingers. The highly elongated middle finger is particularly important for finding food. First, the aye-aye taps on a tree trunk to listen for insect grubs that have bored into the wood. Then the aye-aye scrapes them out with its long, pointed claw-like finger. However, apart from insects, the aye-aye also eats fruits.

Loris and galagos (bush babies)

The loris family consists of about ten species. They live in southern India, Africa, Southeast Asia and its neighbouring islands. The first group belonging to the loris family – the **Loris** and **Golden Potto** – include very slow animals, which grow to the size of a guinea pig or a cat, and have a short tail or no tail at all. In contrast, the second group consists of various **Galagos**. They have long arms and legs and a long tail. In comparison to the lorises, they are a little smaller but much livelier, and they climb and jump habitually.

Both loris groups have large forward-facing eyes. They mainly forage at night for insects, birds and plants, but also small reptiles.

Slow loris
Range: **South to Southeast Asia**
Habitat: **dense rainforests**

Crowned lemur
Range: **Madagascar**
Habitat: **forest regions**

Lemurs

Almost 100 species of lemur or potto live on the island of Madagascar and the neighbouring Comoros.

The best-known lemur, which can also be seen in our zoos, is called the ring-tailed lemur. It has a grey-brown coat, and a long bushy tail with black and white rings. The length of its body is about 45 cm and the length of the tail is 55 cm.

The **Ring-Tailed Lemur** has large eyes and triangular-shaped ears. For the most part, they walk on all fours with their tail erect. Sometimes, they can also be seen climbing through the trees; however, trees are seldom to be found in rocky terrain.

Both males and females have scent glands located on various parts of their body, with which they mark their territories. But anything unfamiliar is also scent-marked.

Up to 40 ring-tailed lemurs live together in one territory. Females stay together with their offspring and the males move on from troop to troop.

After mating, a gestation period of about 130 days follows, after which a single infant (sometimes even two or three) is born. At birth, the infants' eyes are already open and they have a silky, thick coat. They are already independent within six months.

The diet of ring-tailed lemurs consists of grass and leaves. But tree-bark resin and fruits are very popular as well.

Land carnivores

With about 270 species, the carnivores (land and marine carnivores) are more diverse in build, size and form than almost any other mammalian order. The first carnivores already existed 65 million years ago. Today, they are widespread all over the world.

Carnivores hunt other animals, in order to feed themselves. Therefore, they are often considered dangerous beasts. As they have been persecuted by humans, the bear, lynx and wolf have already been largely wiped out in Europe.

Despite the obvious huge differences, land carnivores have many similarities. Their sensory organs are well developed, particularly their sense of smell and their hearing. In addition, many of them have spatial vision. All land carnivores have a mouth equipped with dagger-like canine teeth and often with fangs. They use them to kill or tear open larger prey.

Land carnivores are particularly fast and agile. The so-called pack animal hunters (wolves) take down their prey by chasing it at full speed; stealth hunters (lions) creep up on their prey and seize it by leaping on it. Exceptions amongst land carnivores are the omnivorous bear and fox. Also, for example, pandas only feed on plants and fruits.

Family life varies amongst land carnivores. Some animals live together both during and after mating, and assist each other in the provision of food and defence. With other species, the males see their offspring as tasty prey.

Belonging to the order of land carnivores is the cat family, with the lion, tiger and panther; the hyena family; the dog family, with the wolf, coyote and fox; the weasel family, with the marten, weasel and polecat; and the bear and small bear families, with the brown bear and raccoon.

Cat family

The cat family belongs to the mammalian order of carnivores. It includes our domestic cats as well as lions, tigers and pumas. They all have the same basic build. Essential characteristics are the strong and yet delicate body, the rounded head, the strong paws, the long tail and the soft coats. Cats have powerful teeth. The large, slightly curved canine teeth or fangs are striking. Next to the canines are small incisors and pointed molars that interlock.

Above all, their claws are important tools for attack and defence.

The cat is a digitigrade, which means that it only walks on its toes.

Domestic cat
Range: **worldwide**
Habitat: **residential areas and surrounding countryside**

The domestic cat is descended from the Egyptian desert cat (wildcat species), which still live in Libya and Egypt today. Domestic cats occupy house and home. The cat either searches for a quiet, comfortable spot in a barn or it lives alongside the occupants of the house. Cats are very trusting and clean animals, and indeed affectionate, but often want to impose their own will.

The claws do not touch the ground as they walk, but are retracted into their sheaths (skin folds). Therefore, cats manage to creep up silently on their prey. Most species of cat are able to swim, but only do so if they have to.

Domestic cat (skeleton)

skull, cervical vertebrae, shoulder blade, pelvis, humerus, radius, ulna, rib, toe bones, kneecap, tail vertebrae, femur, fibula, tarsal, metatarsal

Domestic cat (anatomy)

brain, oesophagus, spinal cord, diaphragm, kidney, bowel, liver, lung, heart, stomach, gall bladder, bladder, womb

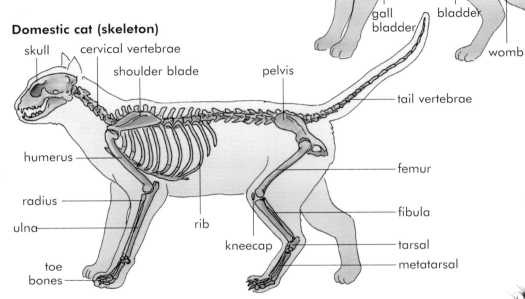

Cats have good hearing and excellent vision. Even over great distances, they can hear footsteps and rustling, long before they spot the prey. Their eyesight is probably not adequate for great distances, but their near vision is excellent. During the daytime, the pupil contracts to a narrow, vertical slit. When it's dark and humans cannot see anything, cats' pupils dilate to form a circle shape. The impact of light is intensified by a reflective layer behind the retina. This leads to their eyes appearing to glow in the dark when they are lit from an external source. In complete darkness, cats find their way with the help of their whiskers, tactile hairs that have nerve endings.

Depending on the species, cats feed on birds, amphibians and fish. Larger species such as cheetahs, lions and so forth eat sheep, cattle and antelopes.

A female cat usually gives birth to a litter of up to six cubs. The mother is responsible for the care of the young. She also defends them, whilst the father only occasionally takes care of them. The cubs learn how to behave in different situations through play, until they are eventually allowed to join the hunt themselves. Once they have become independent, they leave their mother and strike out on their own.

Lion

Lions are also members of the cat family. It is not without reason that the lion is called the 'king of beasts'. Therefore, a fully grown male cuts an impressive figure. A male measuring 2.70 m from the head to the end of the tail weighs up to 250 kg. His mane makes him appear very much bigger and more imposing than the female.

Unlike all other cats, the lion is not a solitary creature, but lives socially in prides of 20–30 animals, of which only one is normally a male. If there are two or three other males, they are descended from a litter within the pride. Lions defend their territory to the last. Any attempt by a male outsider to infiltrate the pride is repelled. If this happens, they let out thunderous roars that can be heard over several kilometres away. Female outsiders are not tolerated by the lionesses either. A male usually stays for only two breeding seasons in the pride, at which point he loses interest in this family, or fails to win a fight against a rival male and so searches for another pride.

During courtship, the male constantly stays close to the female.

About every two years, a lioness has a litter of between two and five cubs. At the end of the gestation period, which lasts for about 110 days, the lioness looks for a concealed spot. It must be near a watering hole and be safe from other predators.

The cubs are blind at birth and have a mottled coat. For the first two months, they live on their mother's milk, and then the lioness takes them with her to hunt. Lion cubs cannot tear up their meat by themselves until they are one year old, once their adult teeth have grown.

After two years, the lioness becomes pregnant again, and then the cubs must leave their mother.

Many cubs do not survive the next few weeks, because they now have to fend for themselves.

Lions usually hunt at dusk and dawn. They doze and sleep during the day. Lionesses are responsible for providing the prey. The male does not normally take part in the hunt. Several lionesses stalk a herd of animals. Initially, they crouch and lie in wait downwind of the prey. Another lioness creeps up on the opposite side. Then suddenly she charges towards the herd and drives the frightened animals towards the lionesses lying in wait. Once the prey is taken down, it is dragged away by the male to a shady spot. The male gets to eat first, followed by the lionesses and only then can the cubs join in. Important prey animals include zebra, gnu, gazelle and antelope. Lions only hunt when they are hungry. Therefore, a grazing herd does not always feel disturbed by a nearby lion. The herd instinctively senses whether the lion is hunting right now or is lethargic and well-fed.

Nowadays lions can only be found in sub-Saharan Africa, and in a small region of India (Gir Forest). Formerly, they lived in Southeast Europe, South Asia and India. The best hope for the survival of lions lies in wildlife reserves and national parks.

Lion family
Range: **sub-Saharan Africa**
Habitat: **savanna and steppe**

Lions live and hunt in a pride consisting of several males, females and their young. The strongest male with a splendid mane around the head, shoulders and chest is the highest-ranking animal.

25

Tiger

Another animal belonging to the cat family is the tiger. The reddish-yellow coat with the black horizontal stripes makes it blend into its surroundings, so that it cannot easily be seen when it moves. There were altogether nine subspecies of tiger, which could be distinguished by the colour of the coat. A tiger has a somewhat lighter and more slender build than a lion. Its average length, including the tail, is about 2.70–2.90 m. The females are a little smaller.

The tiger's coat is short and smooth, and the cheeks are framed by a beard. Tigers living in the more northern regions have a longer and thicker coat than those in the hot regions of India. The tiger's range is not just restricted to India, as has been generally assumed. Tigers can be found between Siberia in the north and Sumatra in the south. The western boundary of their habitat lies in South Caucasus, and the eastern boundary on the Pacific. They live in the jungle, on the steppes, in scrub and in forests. Each tiger has its own territory, which it marks with strong-smelling urine and secretions from glands. It also claws tree bark, which is another kind of boundary marking. Tigers require a large hunting territory: males need about 55 km², whilst females need a somewhat smaller territory.

The tiger usually hunts before dawn and after dusk. It stalks the prey, and initially observes it. Then, like a shot, it attacks the prey from behind or from the side. The tiger drives its claws into the neck of the prey, so that it immediately falls to the ground.

Tigers kill smaller animals by a bite to the neck with their sharp canine teeth.

The tiger suffocates larger animals by biting them on the throat. Before the tiger drags its prey into the undergrowth, it licks the blood flowing from the wound. If the tiger has gorged itself, it sometimes sleeps for more than a day. It will only stir to go to the watering hole. Riverbanks are a favourite spot for catching prey, because every animal comes here to drink and wash.

At the age of three to four, the **Bengal Tiger** becomes sexually mature. Mating takes place in spring, when a male from a neighbouring territory enters the territory of the female. He stays there with the female for about one to three months, as the female is fertile for just one week during this time. Later, the male returns to his own territory. After a gestation period of 15 weeks, a litter of between two and four cubs is born. The cubs are blind for the first ten days. They are suckled by their mother for another eight weeks and then she provides them with small prey items.

After six months, the cubs also stay on their own for days, whilst

Tiger	Range: **between Siberia in the north and Sumatra in the south**
	Habitat: **forests and jungles**

26

the mother is out hunting.

When the cubs are a year old, they go hunting alone, and a few months later they are able to take down large prey themselves. Tigers hunt monkeys, wild boars, lizards, antelopes and deer; in fact anything except the largest animals, such as elephants or rhinoceroses. However, tigers are also hunted: by humans. The revenue earned from capturing a tiger is not inconsiderable, because the meat is said to give courage and strength; it is also used to make medicines. The tiger's coat is tanned and finds its way to China and Europe to be sold. The tiger can only be saved from extinction through a wildlife conservation programme.

Puma

The puma is also a member of the cat family. Its slender body can reach 160 cm in length, with the length of the tail being 65 cm. The puma's coat is mainly silver-grey. In some regions, the colour also takes on a reddish-yellow shade. Generally, the puma has a thick, short coat, with no mane.

The puma has a wide geographical range. Not only can it be found in South America, but also in Mexico, the United States and Canada. Pumas are mainly forest-dwellers, preferring the forest edge, and the adjoining plains, covered in tall grass which provides the perfect environment to hunt. Where there are no trees, pumas hide in the tall grass.

During the day, the puma is usually found sleeping up a tree or in the bushes. It goes out on hunting forays at dawn and dusk, in the course of which it often covers long distances. The puma moves effortlessly and powerfully, and can jump up to six metres. When it spots prey, the puma initially watches it from a tree or an overhanging rock. Then it pounces on the prey: first of all, the puma rips open the prey's neck, and then licks the blood. Smaller animals are completely consumed, whilst larger animals are only partially eaten. When the puma is full up, it retreats to a hiding place and sleeps. In the event that the puma does not

Puma
Range: **south-west Canada to South America**
Habitat: **grassland, mountains and forests**

catch any fresh prey the following night, it returns and eats the leftovers from the previous day. But if it manages to make another kill, it leaves the carrion unattended. Above all, pumas are partial to the blood of an animal. Sometimes, the puma kills several sheep in one night and only feeds on the blood, but not the meat.

Pumas prey on sheep, deer, calves, hares, lynxes and even rheas and monkeys. After a gestation period of three months, the female puma gives birth to several cubs in a hideaway, for example in a rock crevice. The mother raises the cubs alone. After about two and a half months, the cubs go hunting with her for the first time. They remain with their mother for one or two years.

Jaguar

The jaguar is the most feared wild cat in the Americas. It can be found in Central and South America. Particularly large species live in Brazil. The jaguar lives in dense jungle, reeds, thicket and coastal forest. If tall grass or rocks provide sufficient cover, it can also be seen in the open country. Jaguars are a rusty yellow colour, becoming lighter towards the belly and the inside of the legs, with distinctive dark spots, which in turn have spots inside them. In addition, there are varieties of jaguar with black coats that are known as black jaguars. Based on a body length of up to 1.85 m, the average size of a male jaguar is 75 cm.

Outside the mating season, jaguars are solitary animals. As only very few examples of jaguars living in the wild can be found, there is just very little information available about their family life.

Jaguars only meet for a short

Jaguar
Range: **Central and South America**
Habitat: **open forest, mountain regions and rainforest**

time to mate, and then the female gives birth to a litter of up to four cubs, after a gestation period of three to four months. Initially, the cubs are blind and very small, weighing only about 900 g.

After 14 days, the cubs open their eyes and begin to explore their surroundings. At six months old, they go hunting with their mother. After two years, the jaguar looks for its own territory to catch prey. It eats forest animals of all sizes that it prefers to hunt at night. Jaguars often climb up trees to lie in wait for their victim, or they creep up close to the prey and take the animal down.

Jaguars are good swimmers. They catch small alligators, turtles or fish, by lying in wait for them on a ledge above the water. Using their paws, they can fling fish out of the water. Then they consume their prey in a hiding place. The number of jaguars has dramatically declined in many areas, in the course of the colonisation and clearing of the forests, but also through hunting. Fortunately, these animals are breeding so successfully in zoos that the threat of extinction has been overcome. Incidentally, jaguars can live up to 22 years of age in captivity.

The American jaguar. Shown is the entirely black variety of an otherwise yellowish-black, spotted big cat. Both colours sometimes occur in the same litter. Jaguars are mostly active at dusk and during the night. They hunt larger vertebrates (animals with backbones) and initially stalk them, before leaping and grabbing them, and then killing them with a bite to the neck.

Cheetah
Range: **Africa, sub-Sahara**
Habitat: **open scrubland, savanna and semi-desert**

Cheetah

The cheetah differs considerably from the type of animal generally associated with the cat family. It does have a long feline tail and head, but it has unusually long legs. The claws on its toes are no longer able to retract. They are short and blunt like a dog's claws through wear and tear. The length of a cheetah's body is about 1.20–1.40 m, plus the length of its tail (60–80 cm). For the most part, the females are somewhat larger than the males.

The cheetah cannot grip its prey – which often consists of deer, gazelles and other antelopes – with its claws. Instead, the cheetah bears down on its prey with its front paws.

In the same way as humans use hunting dogs to catch prey, cheetahs undertook this role in parts of Asia and Africa for

Cheetahs live alone or in groups. If they live in the group, then they also hunt larger animals as a team. First, they stalk the prey and then run it down after a short, quick sprint. Afterwards, they bite it on the neck. However, if they do not succeed in catching the prey within a short amount of time, they give up.

thousands of years. For this purpose, only animals that have already learnt how to hunt from their mother are captured and tamed.

As the fastest mammal, the cheetah can reach a speed of about 80 km/h over short distances, and in extreme cases even 100 km/h, whilst making jumps of over six metres in length. After lying in wait for the prey, the cheetah chases it over short distances at this speed. If it succeeds in pulling the animal to the ground, first it rests for a short while and then begins to eat the prey.

The female cheetah is ready to mate about every eight to ten days over a period of two weeks. Following mating, a litter of up to six cubs is born, after a gestation period of 90–95 days.

Cheetahs are found throughout sub-Saharan regions, where they inhabit savannas, semi-deserts, and plains with open scrubland.

Leopard

The leopard and the jaguar are similar in colour, markings and build. It has a very large range: this includes South Asia and Africa, where it lives in deserts, mountains, rainforests and savannas.

The total length of a leopard is about 240 cm, of which the tail alone measures 70 cm. It has a powerful body and a roundish head. The magnificent coat is a reddish-yellow colour, which becomes lighter towards the belly. Numerous spots covering the body make the animal look strikingly colourful at first. However, the colour of its coat matches the hues of the soil and vegetation of its habitat so well that this predator can only be detected on closer inspection.

Leopards prefer to stay in forests with dense undergrowth. They also find places to hide and to hunt in the mountains. The leopard is not the fastest predator, but it can make giant leaps and climb very well. It hunts baboons up trees, which prevents these animals from becoming too numerous.

The leopard's staple diet includes goats, chickens, antelopes and sheep. It often kills several animals in one night. Therefore, stock farmers fear them more than lions, because a lion snatches an animal once a night, at most. As reported by naturalists, leopards enter villages, and even go into huts, searching for prey. For the most part, leopards do not attack humans.

When the female is ready to mate, she leaves her penetrating, strong-smelling urine behind on trees. The male is attracted to her scent and remains for about a week, until they have finished mating. Afterwards, the female is by herself again. After a gestation period of 90–110 days, she gives birth to a litter of two to six cubs, which are initially blind, and raises them alone. But usually only one or two per litter survive. Initially, she frequently carries the cubs to a new hiding place, so that they are not eaten by hyenas or lions. After a few months, the cubs learn how to hunt and fend for themselves.

In addition, black panthers still share the same genes and characteristics as leopards, and are in no respect different from leopards of the standard colour, except for the colour of their coat. The black panther should not be confused with the black jaguar.

Leopard
Range: **Africa, Central and South Asia**
Habitat: **desert, forests and mountains**

Dog family

The dog family are also carnivores. Many of them live in packs and have large territories in which they hunt. They often cover long distances at great speed to catch

African wild dog
Range: **sub-Saharan Africa**
Habitat: **steppe, semi-desert and mountain regions**

Wild dogs live together in packs of up to 30 animals. When they are hunting for prey, they cover large areas and only stay in one place if it is impossible for the pups to carry on any further.

Domestic dog (golden retriever)
Range: **different breeds in many parts of the world**
Habitat: **alongside humans for companionship or as working dogs**

Domestic dogs, which represent a tamed form of the wolf, can be divided into about 400 breeds, and in accordance with particular similarities are assigned to different breed groups. Examples of these classifications include terriers, spaniels, cattle dogs and sheepdogs.

prey. This is especially true for larger relatives of the dog. When they are out hunting as a pack, they surround their victim and overpower it as a team. In this way, animals that are larger than themselves can be hunted too.

Although dogs do not have sharp vision, they can see at night due to their sensitivity to light. Their sense of smell is particularly well developed. A dog can smell a human being from as far as several hundred metres away. It can follow tracks that are not fresh and detect the direction in which someone has gone by the intensity of the odour. A dog's hearing is also extremely pronounced. Every little sound catches their attention, whereby they immediately prick up their ears, raise their head and start growling or barking. Dogs have particularly well-developed teeth. The canine teeth have evolved into sharp fangs and moreover the carnassials are ideally suited to biting through pieces of meat. However, apart from meat, dogs also eat plant material, as their

back molars have wide chewing surfaces.

Members of the dog family are digitigrades, which means that they walk with their four toes touching the ground (both front and back legs). But unlike cats, their claws are fixed and not retractable, and therefore wear down when they walk. Dogs do not use their claws when they fight.

Members of the dog family include the wolf, jackal, fox, African wild dog and, of course, the domestic dog and hunting dog.

Jackal

Jackals live in the African savanna and in the scrubland of Southeast Europe and South Asia. The most common jackal is the **Black-Backed Jackal**, whose build is similar to that of a dog. The length of its body can grow up to about one metre, and its tail is about 30 cm long. For the most part, it has a reddish-brown coat, which is sometimes grey. The jackal has a saddle of greyish-black fur on its back, which clearly sets it apart from other jackal species.

In areas uninhabited by humans,

jackals hunt during the day and night as a team. In other areas, it only hunts at dusk and during the night. They catch small animals, but also eat fruits, berries and carrion (dead animals). Carrion is always a particularly welcome meal. When lions or tigers have ripped apart a large prey animal, there is often something left over for jackals.

After a gestation period of about nine weeks, the female jackal gives birth to a litter of up to six pups.

Jackal
Range: **Southeast Europe, South Asia and Africa**
Habitat: **scrubland**

The male jackal lives alongside the female. Several jackal pairs raise their pups together.

Other jackal species are the **Golden Jackal**, which is somewhat smaller than the **black-backed jackal** – and owing to its appearance it was formerly considered to be the ancestor of our domestic dog – and the **Side-Striped Jackal**, which stands out on account of the black stripes on the sides of its grey coat, as well as the white tip of its tail.

Wolves are an endangered species, because they are persecuted by humans. They occupy a territory which is some 100 km² in size and whose boundaries are scent-marked with urine. Wolves frequently hunt for prey as a team. Then they surround their victim and pursue it over many kilometres if need be, because although wolves are not particularly fast, they are very persistent.

Wolf
Range: **northern Europe, Canada and Russia**
Habitat: **arctic tundra, steppe and woodlands**

Wolf

The wolf, which is a member of the dog family, is the best-known wild dog. In the past, different breeds were found throughout large parts of Europe, Asia and North America. Today, it has been wiped out in many regions.

The wolf is a muscular and powerful animal. The colour of its coat is grey-brown, reddish-brown or black, in accordance with the region it inhabits. The coat is almost white in polar regions.

Larger species with a body length of 1.40 m are heavier than 75 kg, whilst smaller species only weigh 15 kg. The females are usually smaller and lighter than the males. Wolves prey on rabbits and hares, birds and rodents. In winter, they even attack moose, deer and reindeer, which they pursue over long distances, until they finally seize the prey with their sharp fangs. Wolves live in packs dominated by a strict hierarchy, which is expressed by particular gestures or postures: for example, a high-ranking male holds its tail higher than the other males. However, a female can also be the dominant wolf. Several family groups and lone wolves often live together within the pack.

The alpha male and female of the pack mate between February and April. After a gestation period of two months, a litter of between three and ten pups is born. The female gives birth in a hiding place, or in a den she has dug out herself. At first, the pups are blind. The pups are suckled for about two months, but even at this age they are occasionally given pieces of meat that their mother regurgitates to supplement their diet. Care of the pups is not only carried out by the mother, but other members of the pack help too. At a year old, wolves are fully grown, and sexually mature at about the age of three. Wolf pairs often stay together for several years. Wolves live for about ten years in the wild and for about fifteen years in captivity.

Coyote

The coyote is a close relative of the wolf, and is also known as prairie wolf. Its range stretches from Alaska to Central America. As the length of a coyote's body is only 90 cm and weighs between 15 and 20 kg, it is considerably lighter than the wolf.

Coyotes live in small packs or wander alone on the prairie and in sparse forests. In spite of being persecuted by humans, and particularly as they breed with their own relative – the wolf – coyote numbers have dramatically increased.

Coyotes mostly prey on rodents and rabbits and are therefore actually beneficial to farmers.

In addition, coyotes eat snakes and insects, as well as berries and grass. They even prey on fish and frogs.

After a gestation period of about 60 days, the coyote cubs are born. The male provides the cubs and the female with food in the following weeks. When the cubs are about six months old, they go in search of their own territory.

Coyote
Range: **from Alaska to Central America**
Habitat: **prairie and sparse woodland**

Fox

The fox, which is also commonly known as 'Reynard the Fox', differs from every other member of the dog family due to a distinguishing feature: the pupil is not round as in the other species, but is vertically slit like that of a cat. Furthermore, the fox is distinguished by its pointed snout, which stands out against the broad head. The fox's fur is a reddish colour on its back, and white on its belly, and the tail (brush) is long and bushy. The fur is lighter and thicker in winter than in summer.

Foxes mostly live in forests or on the edges of forests, where they can easily reach open country. They make their home in an underground den, which a male and female pair occupies together temporarily. Their den consists of different burrows on several levels, which are connected through a system of tunnels, and have several exits to the ground above. They inhabit it throughout the year.

A fox's territory covers a radius of 3–4 km around its den. During the day, the fox usually sleeps in its den, and goes hunting at night. Then it creeps up on the prey, before pouncing and catching it.

The fox's staple diet is the mouse. Sometimes, it also catches rabbits and hares or chickens and raids birds' nests. Even frogs, beetles and snails, as well as potatoes and turnips, are on the menu. After the mating season in January or February, a litter of four to eight pups is born in May. Before giving birth to her cubs, the female fox (vixen) digs a breeding earth, and uses the hair on her belly as soft padding to line it. She suckles the cubs for eight weeks. During this period, the male fox (dog) tends to the vixen and also later to the cubs. Through play and their first outings to explore their territory, the cubs learn how to hunt and find food.

Red fox
Range: **North America, Europe, Asia, Australia**
Habitat: **embankments, forest edges and fields**

Hyena family

Hyenas live in Southwest Asia and Africa. These animals are more closely related to the cat family, although their build suggests that they belong to the dog family.

Hyenas have a large head and an especially powerful jaw, so that they are able to crush even the biggest bones. Their forelegs are longer than their hind legs and therefore their back slopes a little. They can neither run nor jump particularly well.

Although in the past it was believed that hyenas only live on carrion and sick animals, more recently it has been observed that the larger species, such as the spotted hyena, even go hunting in packs for antelopes or zebras. Initially, the prey is taken down by a bite to the leg.

Hyenas mainly go hunting in the early morning. Once they have finally overpowered and killed their prey, they start their famous howling and laughing.

The largest hyena species is the **Spotted Hyena**. It can grow to about 1.60 m in length and weigh 80 kg. Their pack, which consists of up to 100 animals, can usually be found in open terrain. They use urine and gland secretions to scent-mark the borders of their territory.

The cubs are born in an underground den. They are suckled for over a year and afterwards are able to go hunting with the pack.

Another hyena species is the **Striped Hyena**, which only grows to about a metre in length and is widespread in Africa and Asia. It eats mainly carrion or smaller animals such as sheep and goats.

The rare **Brown Hyena** lives in South Africa. It is also known as the **Strandwolf**. Their staple diet consists of animal carcasses, birds and chickens, but also mussels and fish. They are an endangered species.

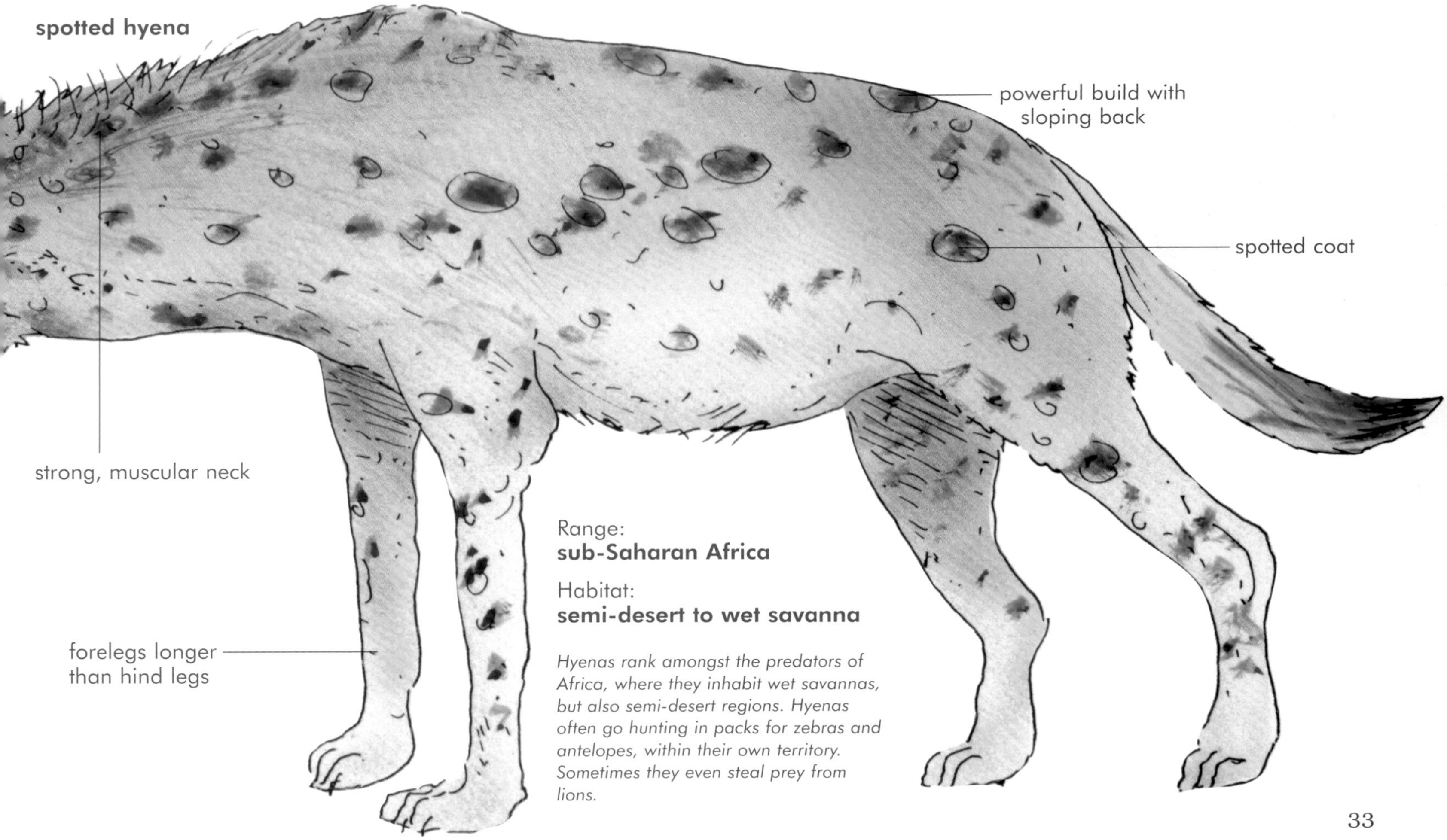

spotted hyena

powerful build with sloping back

spotted coat

strong, muscular neck

forelegs longer than hind legs

Range:
sub-Saharan Africa

Habitat:
semi-desert to wet savanna

Hyenas rank amongst the predators of Africa, where they inhabit wet savannas, but also semi-desert regions. Hyenas often go hunting in packs for zebras and antelopes, within their own territory. Sometimes they even steal prey from lions.

Weasel family

The weasel family can be found throughout the world, as far as Australia and Madagascar. It consists of about 58 species of small to medium-sized mammals. Most weasels have a slender, flexible body and a long tail. They are good climbers.

All weasels produce secretions from their scent glands to mark their territory. In many species, these powerful scents are even used for defence. Members of the weasel family include the polecat, stoat, weasel, wolverine and otter.

Polecat
Range:
Europe
Habitat:
forest

Otter
Range:
Europe, North Africa and northern Russia
Habitat: **open wetlands, streams and riverbanks, lakes**

Pine marten

The pine marten lives in Europe and Western Asia. Its body is 35 cm long and it has a dark-brown coat with a light-yellow patch on the neck and throat. The silky fur is considered to be of great value. The pine marten uses its long, bushy tail to manoeuvre when it jumps. The short legs with their short toes have sharp claws.

Pine marten
Range: **Europe, Western Asia**
Habitat: **woodland**

Pine martens mostly go hunting at night. They clamber, leap and race through the trees, catching squirrels and birds. But also rabbits and young deer must be wary of the pine marten. Sometimes when pine martens are very hungry, they also break into dovecotes or henhouses, where they kill everything they find. They instinctively grab any prey that moves. In addition, pine martens eat berries and fruits in autumn.

During the day, the pine marten hides in a hollow tree or beneath a pile of wood.

After a gestation period of about six months, the female gives birth to a litter of between two and seven kits. The kits are independent after about four months and are sexually mature when they are two years old.

Otter

Otters are also members of the weasel family, and are very well-adapted to an aquatic life. Although they have the slender build of a weasel, they also have a fleshy, muscular tail, which they use to propel themselves through the water. They have four webbed feet. The short, dense coat keeps the skin dry, because it traps the air to form an insulating layer around the whole body. Otters can move well on land, whilst in the water they are excellent divers and swimmers, hunting for fish, frogs and other aquatic animals. In addition, voles and waterfowl are on the menu.

Hunting mostly takes place at night. During the day, the animals live in their dens along riverbanks. Otters are very playful creatures that slide down the riverbanks full of joy. In spring – at any time of year in southern latitudes – a litter of between two and three pups is born, after a gestation period of about 60 days. Otters are 50–80 cm long, and their tail measures 30–50 cm. They are an endangered species, because they are viewed by fishermen as competitors.

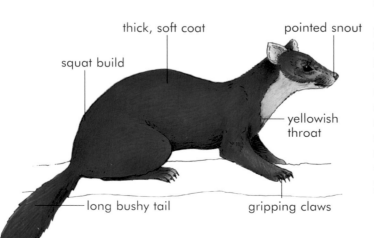

thick, soft coat

pointed snout

squat build

yellowish throat

long bushy tail

gripping claws

Otters are solitary animals and can only very rarely be observed. Their geographical range covers Europe (except for many Mediterranean islands), North Africa and Asia.

tunnels with individual nest chambers, which are lined with grasses and fragments of plants. This is where the females also give birth to between two and four cubs, after a gestation period of about one year.

Badgers usually remain in their setts during the day. They play and scuffle outside at night. They eat fruits, nuts, earthworms, mice, frogs and young rabbits.

The **Honey Badger** is a particular species of badger native to Africa. It eats honey and grubs and is helped in the process by a bird called the honeyguide. The bird searches for bees' nests and guides the honey badger to the spot by calling (so that it can feast on the remaining wax and grubs). The honey badger then opens up the nests with its front paws, which are equipped with long sharp claws for digging.

Now the badger and the honeyguide can both enjoy the meal together. The honey badger has a particularly hard skin, which protects it from bee stings.

sleep. Skunks become lively at night and search for prey, which consists of insects, amphibians, birds and small rodents. The skunk only uses its foul-smelling secretions from its glands as a defensive weapon, in the event that it is provoked or chased. Then it will raise its tail and spray the fluid directly away from its body. If the skunk is directly attacked, then it sprays the fluid straight at the animal, to repel it. The smell sticks to the enemy's fur for weeks.

Badger
Range: **Europe and Asia**
Habitat:
embankments, fields, moors, hedges and woods

Striped skunk
Range:
North America
Habitat:
sparse forests, grassland

Badger

The badger is an inelegant animal with a stocky body and is a member of the weasel family. The length of its body is between 60 and 90 cm. The badger has a short tail and large paws with powerful claws for digging. The top half of the body is grey, and it is black underneath. The black and white striped head is largely shaped like a snout.
The **European Badger** lives in huge underground setts, which it excavates with its claws.

To make their setts, badgers use branches to construct a system of

Skunk

The skunk is one of the best-known relatives of the weasel. Using secretions from its glands, it can distribute an atrocious stench. Skunks have a long, slender body with a dark ground colour and white stripes. The tail is covered in long thick hairs. They inhabit the steppe-like regions of America.

During the day, skunks mostly shelter in dens they have dug out themselves that are located in rock crevices or hollow trees, where they

The skunk is a distant relative of the weasel, and lives on mice, eggs, insects, berries and carrion. The odour it emits from scent glands close to the anus is notorious. The skunk unleashes this odour to repel its enemies.

After a gestation period of 60–75 days, the females give birth to a litter of between two and five (seldom eight) kits in hidden dens lined with plant material.

Different species of skunk are the **White-Backed Skunk (Hooded Skunk)** in South America, the **Striped Skunk** in North America and the **Spotted Skunk** in the western USA.

Wolverine

The wolverine is a member of the weasel family and is native to all northern countries around the North Pole. It has a reputation of being a particularly aggressive and ferocious predator. The wolverine's fur is long and thick. The coat is dark brown with light-coloured stripes on the sides of the body, the head and the top of the tail. With a body measuring 70–100 cm in length and a heavily built frame, the wolverine is also able to kill animals that are much larger than it is. Wolverines eat rodents and birds, but do not shy away from attacking moose or roe deer as well. It catches them in a surprise attack, by pouncing on the prey from a tree or rocks.

There are also instances when the wolverine snatches prey from wolves whilst they are devouring it, and chases them away. On account of the wolverine's offensive smell, spread by the scent glands, it actually succeeds.

Wolverines live in large territories, which are each inhabited by a male and two or three females. After a gestation period of seven to nine months, in spring the female gives birth to a litter of two or three kits in a den. The kits, which initially have a light-coloured coat, are suckled for about eight weeks. They remain with their mother for two years, and thereafter they must search for their own territory.

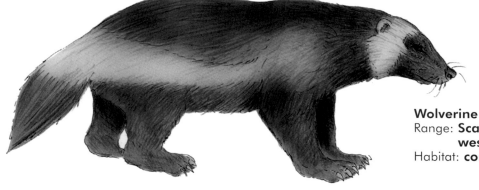

Wolverine
Range: **Scandinavia, Siberia, Alaska, Canada, western USA**
Habitat: **coniferous forest, tundra**

Large bear family

The black bear or baribal has a glossy black to dark-brown coat. It is usually only active at night when it goes on extensive forays, searching for fruits, berries, nuts, roots and honey. In addition, the black bear eats insects, rodents and other small mammals, fish swimming upstream and sometimes even carrion and waste material.

Large bears are carnivores that live in the warmest but also the coldest regions of our planet. They are found in high mountain regions, but also by the icy sea. They are solitary animals. The grizzly bear, polar bear, black bear and brown bear are all members of the large bear family.

Bears have a large and thickset body. They have a large head and short legs. Their coat is thick and either light brown or dark brown to black, depending on the species; the only exception is the polar bear, which has a cream-coloured coat. They have five toes with long, curved claws on each of their back and front paws. The claws are not retractable as in the case of cats, and are therefore usually heavily worn down. Bears are plantigrades and walk with the entire soles of the feet on the ground.

All bears living in temperate zones feast during the summer to put on a layer of fat in preparation for the cold winter. They are omnivores and feed on berries, fruits, grass and roots. In addition, they hunt fish, crabs, birds and mammals. If they are ravenous, the larger bears amongst them even attack bigger animals such as cattle or horses. As bears are omnivores, they have wide back molars to grind up the plants in their diet, in addition to canine teeth.

Bears dig out a den in the ground for the cold winter months, provided that there are no natural dens or rock crevices available. They line one area of this den with leaves, moss and grass, so that they have a soft bed to rest in. Polar bears bury themselves under a thick layer of snow and build their den in it.

After mating, the female retires to a den, where, depending on the species, she gives birth to between one and six cubs, after a gestation period of 6–8 months. The cubs are blind at birth. They are suckled, looked after, protected and cared for by their mother.

Black bear
Range:
North America
Habitat:
forest regions, marshland

Brown bear

The brown bear has the largest range of all the large bears. In Europe, it can often only be found in Scandinavia, and in the Balkan peninsula and Russia. In addition, it can be found in parts of Asia, western Canada and Alaska. The term brown bear covers different subspecies, such as the Kodiak bear or grizzly bear (also called the silvertip bear).

The brown bear can grow up to two and a half metres, and they are therefore one of the largest carnivores. They can weigh up to 650 kg. Bears are solitary animals, but also live in small family groups. Their coat is a brownish-black colour. The mouth, which has particularly powerful canine teeth, is worthy of mention.

Brown bears are only active at night in some regions, because in the past they were constantly hunted during the day. Then they search for nuts, berries, roots and fruits, but also fish, insects and small vertebrates. Salmon are a particular delicacy in Alaska. Salmon swim in large numbers through specific regions during their migration and the bears hurl them out of the water with their powerful paws.

Brown bears build up fat reserves during the summer, which they live off during winter hibernation in their den.

Every two or three years, the female brown bear gives birth to a litter of up to four cubs, after a

Brown bear
Range: **Europe, Asia, North America**
Habitat: **forest, tundra**

gestation period of about 6–8 months. The cubs are blind at birth and are very small, weighing only about 400–700 g each. They remain with their mother for at least a year.

Polar bear

The polar bear is native to the Arctic Ocean. This huge animal, which can grow up to three meters, has a shaggy, cream-coloured coat, under which a thick layer of fat is stored. Therefore, the polar bear is untroubled by the icy cold weather of its habitat. In spite of its enormous size, the polar bear is very fast. When hunting prey, it can run at speeds of up to 50 km/h. The polar bear is also a persistent and skilled hunter in water.

Polar bears have been sighted in the open sea even in excess of 100 km from dry land, where they are on the lookout for seals resting on floes of drift ice. Once the seals have been spotted, polar bears approach them from under the water, so that they can then spring up in front of them at lightning speed. Besides seals, their most important prey is fish (salmon), arctic hares and arctic foxes. Polar bears frequently go ashore during the summer, where they eat leaves and fruits (for example blueberries) – which grow in the tundra – as well as moose.

Polar bears do not enter into a state of deep hibernation during the winter. They simply hibernate in winter and wake up from time to time, but they do not leave their den. They live off their layer of fat, which is 3–4 cm thick, until the end of winter.

Polar bears are usually solitary animals. Mating takes place during the summer. The female makes a nest for the cubs in autumn. This is usually built on a slope with fresh snowfall, because she builds a den there from the thick layer of new snow. Six months later, she gives birth to usually two, but sometimes up to four, cubs in the den. The cubs are initially blind and the size of a kitten. They stay with their mother for the next two years, learning how to swim and hunt.

Polar bear
Range: **southern border of the arctic pack ice**
Habitat: **shoreline and icebergs**

Small bear family

The small bear family is a separate group of carnivores. About 16 species belong to this group and they are native to the temperate and tropical climates of North and South America. For the most part, they are the size of a fox with an elongated and somewhat squat body. They are similar to weasels or large bears.

Small bears can climb well. Many of them live in the trees. Some of them only eat meat, whilst others eat plants. Small bears include the raccoon and coati.

The endangered red panda belongs to a specific family of small bears, which are also called the red cat-bear (or lesser panda). They can be found in southwest or central China.

**Lesser panda
(red panda, red cat-bear)
Range: Southeast Asia to Southwest China
Habitat: bamboo forests**

Raccoon

The raccoon is primarily native to Central and North America, where it lives in forests and marshy areas and often on the shores of lakes and other stretches of water.

The raccoon can grow to about 60 cm in size and its bushy tail is 25 cm long. It has a thick, grey-flecked coat, the colour of which is interrupted by black rings on the tail. The raccoon is easy to recognise by the dark 'mask' against the light-coloured face and the pointed snout. Raccoons hold their food with the long delicate fingers on their forelegs. Their diet includes rodents, eggs, fruits and seeds. Raccoons can still detect their prey even in the most secluded hiding places. Raccoons particularly like sitting on a riverbank and catching crabs, frogs and fish. They hold small pieces of food between their front paws and wash them in the water.

Once raccoons have mated, the female gives birth to a litter of between three and five cubs, after a gestation period of about 60–65 days. The cubs are blind at birth and for the first three weeks. After just two months, the cubs can be seen roaming with their mother through the forests.

**Raccoon
Range: North and Central America
Habitat: forest regions along stretches of water**

Coati

The coati is a member of the small bear family (raccoon family) and lives in Central and South America, where it can be found in groups of more than 30 animals. They are very adaptable and can live in the tropical rainforest as well as in dry mountains or deserts.

A coati's body is between 45 and 65 cm in length. The tail is almost as long, and is also bushy with dark-brown stripes. Coatis hold their tail erect when they walk. The most striking feature of this powerful animal is its pointed, flexible nose or snout, which enables the coati to search for food in the narrowest rock crevices. Its diet includes spiders, insects and worms. However, the coati also eats fruit, mice and lizards. Coatis

forage for food during the day and night. They prefer to rest only at midday when the sun is at its hottest.

Groups of coatis separate shortly after mating. The females now live separately until they give birth to a litter of up to seven kits, after a gestation period of about 70 days. The kits are usually born in a rock crevice or in a nest up a tree. Initially, they still live alone with their mother and join the group of one-year-old coatis after a few months.

Older males only stay in the group during the mating season. Whilst they have no specific role, they are, however, subordinate to the females.

Coati
Range:
Central and South America
Habitat:
forest regions, lowland forests

long striped tail

muscular body

short legs

trunk-like, pointed snout

long sharp claws

Giant panda/panda bear

The **Giant Panda**, which has become famous as it is the symbol of the World Wide Fund for Nature (WWF), can almost never be found in the wild. The population has shrunk to 1,500 animals. The panda is a member of the large bear family. With its bear-like build, it grows to a height of 1.50 m. The soft coat is black and white. The panda uses elongated wrist bones (functioning rather like thumbs) to grip with its front paws so that it can easily hold bamboo shoots, which make up the panda's diet. Because bamboo shoots and stalks contain only very few nutrients, pandas have to spend most of the day eating. The giant panda is believed to be the only living

Panda
Range: **mountainous regions in China**
Habitat:
bamboo forests

carnivore that is a vegetarian. The giant panda is a solitary animal with its own territory. During the mating season, the panda searches for a female outside its territory, which he courts and attracts by making low wailing sounds. Any cub born from their union is blind at birth and only weighs just over 100 g! Yet after just two months, the cub has increased its weight twentyfold. Panda bears move around on the ground for most of the day. When they are in danger, they climb up trees.

The **Lesser Panda**, which is also called the red panda or the red cat-bear, has a reddish-brown coat with a striped, bushy tail. It has particularly striking white markings on the face. The lesser panda also mainly feeds on bamboo. But in addition, the animal eats berries, roots and acorns and sometimes even young birds. It lives in bamboo forests and in the foothills of the Himalayas. However, the lesser panda is not closely related to the giant panda.

39

Insectivores

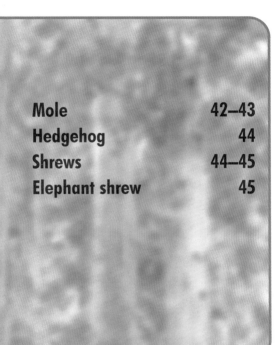

About 450 species of insectivores (insect-eaters) also belong to the mammalian order. There are small, timid creatures that only grow to between 3.5 cm and 45 cm in size, depending on the species. Some insectivores have a soft velvety coat whereas others have a spiny one.

A distinguishing feature of insectivores is their pointed snout, and a mouth containing many small, pointed and sharp teeth. Their hearing and sense of smell are usually well developed. Many species can even produce ultrasonic sounds and use the returning echo to navigate.

The earliest insectivores lived as much as 100 million years ago during the Cretaceous period; from them all mammalian orders – ranging from humans to elephants – are said to have evolved.

Nearly all insectivores are solitary animals. Many of them live underground or in concealed hiding places. They often have a network of burrows or tunnels beneath the earth, in which they move around. Some species live by the water or in trees. Insectivores feed on snails, beetles and grubs, but also on small rodents.

Insectivores can be found throughout the world, except for Australia and polar regions.

Members of the insectivore family include the hedgehog, shrew, mole and solenodon.

Mole

The mole belongs to the mammalian order of insectivores. It can be found throughout Europe and a part of North America and Asia. It spends almost its entire life underground.

Wherever the mole finds moist, loose soil such as fields, meadows and gardens, it creates a large number of runways just under the surface of the earth, which can be easily recognized by the molehills appearing above ground. The mole crawls through its runway system several times a day in order to search for food. The mole's actual home, which is called the burrow, is situated under a larger molehill. It is well lined with grass, leaves and moss. The burrow can often be found beyond the runway systems, which the mole uses for hunting purposes. Then a sturdy entrance called the runway leads to the burrow.

The mole's frame is superbly adapted to living underground: the squat, cylindrical body (altogether 15 cm long) merges into a small head without any visible connecting neck, and together with the nose extends to a kind of pointed trunk.

The eyes and ears are barely visible as they are so shrivelled. The mole's mouth has sharp teeth, which sets it apart as an insectivore.

The mole's coat is thick and velvety in order to repel water and particles of soil. The individual hairs of its coat do not fall in any particular direction so that the animal can easily move forwards and backwards. The body is supported by four limbs and the forelimbs are used as shovels.

The upper arms and forearms are quite short. They disappear into the body completely so that only the hands protrude from under the fur and stick out horizontally to each side, with their wide palms facing backwards. The short fingers, which are fused together with skin, have sharp, large claws. The rear limbs are only poorly developed and are not

mole hill

involved in digging.

When engaged in burrowing activities, the mole also uses its head – with the fleshy trunk-like snout – to clear the way. At the same time, both the mouth and the ear canals are tightly sealed by a fold of skin. If the soil is too hard, then the mole draws back its head a long way, so that the hands can reach further forwards than the head and can loosen the mass of

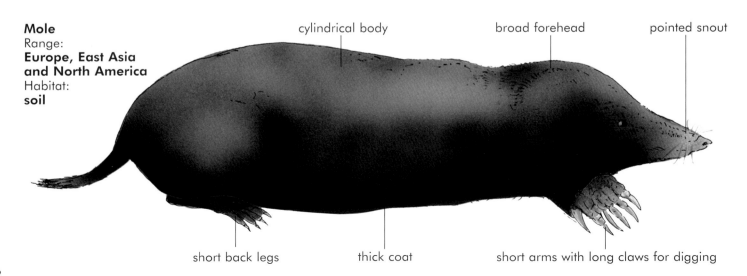

Mole
Range:
Europe, East Asia and North America
Habitat:
soil

cylindrical body

broad forehead

pointed snout

short back legs

thick coat

short arms with long claws for digging

Mole (skeleton)

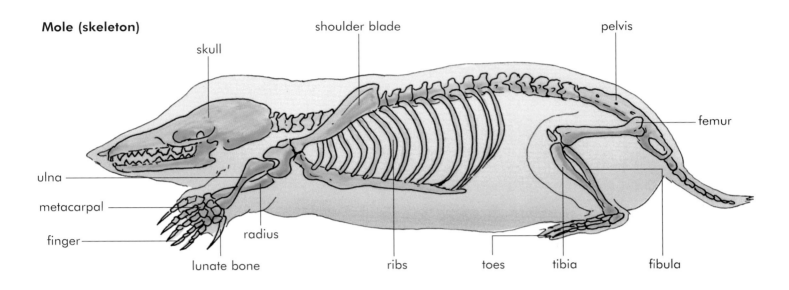

At the beginning of winter, moles burrow into deeper layers of the soil that are free of frost. For this period, they collect and store worms, which they paralyse by a bite to the head segment.

In addition to humans, moles have numerous other enemies, including the polecat, falcon, buzzard, owl and stork.

However, moles are also useful to humans, because by killing mice and insect grubs they keep their numbers within reasonable limits.

soil. When too much loose soil has accumulated, the mole uses its head to push it upwards. As a result we see molehills appearing on the surface.

Depending on the firmness of the soil, moles can excavate at between 5 and 10 m per hour.

A mole's diet consists mainly of earthworms, insects and insect grubs, which it finds beneath the soil. As moles have an excellent sense of smell, they can easily detect them. Moles sometimes come up to the surface at night where they can catch snails and other small creatures. For example, mice are a welcome treat. Moles need a great deal of food, due to their laborious burrowing activities that drain their energy. On a daily basis, they eat about as much as they weigh themselves, and sometimes even two to three times their own weight.

The mole digs out pits close to its burrow, which fill up with rain water. In this way, a supply of drinking water is ensured.

Every mole has its own territory. If another animal ever manages to gain access to the mole's runway system, it results in a fight. The fight continues until there is only one survivor, which then eats the victim.

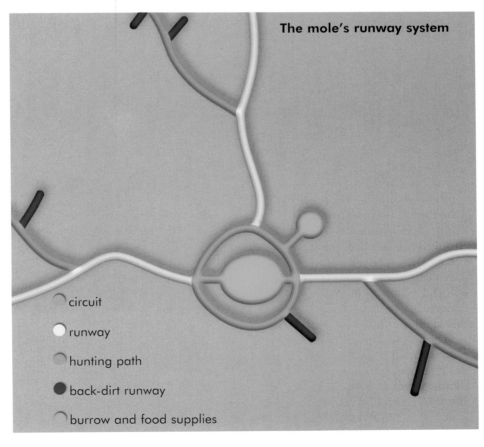

The mole's runway system

○ circuit
○ runway
○ hunting path
● back-dirt runway
○ burrow and food supplies

Hedgehog

Hedgehog
Range:
Europe, Asia and Africa
Habitat:
**deciduous forests and mixed forests
hedgerows and farmland**

The hedgehog is a nocturnal animal, which belongs to the order of insectivores. It is found throughout Europe (except in the coldest countries), Asia and Africa.

The hedgehog has a roundish body of about 30 cm in length, weighs about 1,200 g and has a spiny coat. It has short legs and a short tail. The hedgehog's habitat ranges from hedges and gardens to forest margins and brush. It establishes a nest in vacated rabbit holes or hollow trees, which it lines with moss and leaves. The hedgehog sleeps there during the day. At night, it goes out on forays within the boundaries of its territory, which can extend over a few hundred metres. The hedgehog searches for snails, worms, beetles or young mice with its pointed snout. A hedgehog will not even spare adders. If the snake attacks it, the hedgehog curls up into a tight ball at lightning speed, and the adder is now confronted with nothing but sharp spines. If it manages to bite through this venomous snake's backbone, then the hedgehog can eat the whole snake. If an adder strikes it in the face, the hedgehog has lost and is killed by the snake's venom. However, wasp and bee stings have no effect on a hedgehog.

If food becomes scarcer in autumn, the hedgehog retires to its warm, lined den and hibernates over winter. During this time, the hedgehog lives off its fat reserves, which it has previously built up.

After mating has taken place between April and July, the hedgehog mother gives birth to a litter of 5–8 young, which initially are suckled for four weeks, but afterwards go foraging with her. Sometimes, a hedgehog mother can be observed with her young toddling on behind her. If a baby hedgehog loses sight of its mother, it makes a whistling sound and the mother goes and fetches it. After about two months, the young have to fend for themselves and they are chased away from the nest.

The hedgehog's enemies are the dog, fox and polecat. The hedgehog can usually manage to roll into a tight ball quickly enough so that these animals no longer stand a chance. However, if the hedgehog is pushed into a puddle of water, it unfurls itself and so can be easily overpowered.

Due to the fact that the hedgehog controls many pests, it is a protected species in the UK.

Shrews

With the exception of Australia, New Zealand and part of South America, shrews are found almost everywhere. Shrews are energetic animals that venture out to forage for food both day and night, whilst

African mouse shrew

Range: **South Africa**
Habitat: **wetlands near woods,
and embankments**

Elephant shrews are very energetic animals. Their metabolic rate is higher than that of other animals. Therefore, their heart beats up to 1,200 times per minute. Many elephant shrews can deter natural predators by releasing pungent secretions.

insects and various small animals. They mainly rely on their sense of smell and their hearing to hunt, because they do not have particularly good sight. Shrews deter their enemies – including hawks and owls – with a foul-smelling secretion from their glands. Some species of shrews are even reported to eat their own droppings and those of other animals as well.

The **Water Shrew**, which is also found in Europe, can swim and dive. It mainly feeds on aquatic insects as well as small fish and tadpoles.

taking only short breaks. They consume a great deal of energy and have to eat their own body weight in food every day. Besides worms, snails and mice, shrews also eat

Water shrew
Range: **most of Europe**
Habitat: **shoreline**

Elephant shrew

Elephant shrews belong to a specific order and have a prominent trunk-like snout just like almost all insectivores. In particular, these mouse- or rat-sized animals use their snout to root around for all kinds of insects and small animals. However, elephant shrews have also been observed eating vegetation.

Their thin, sinewy and long back legs are evidence of these animals' agility as 'jumping shrews'; furthermore, they are longer than the front legs. Elephant shrews have a particularly distinctive build. Without the characteristic trunk-like snout, they could be taken for gerbils. However, all the other 20 species of elephant shrew can also hop long distances. In the event of danger, some species thump on the ground with their

Short-eared elephant shrew
Range: **Namibia and South Africa**
Habitat: **plains, rocky landscapes**

feet, in order to warn their fellow creatures. Yet unlike the gerbil, the elephant shrew can be found in the savanna and the rainforest. Native to Africa, they are hardly ever active during the day. Most elephant shrews sleep through the heat of the day in burrows and only come to the surface at dusk. All species are brownish in colour, to a greater

or lesser extent, and therefore difficult to distinguish.

The reddish-brown golden-rumped elephant shrew is the largest species in the elephant shrew family. This shrew can clearly be distinguished from the other categories by the size of its body and the structure of its teeth. They live in east Africa.

45

Rodents, rabbits and hares

There are about 5,500 species of mammal in existence, of which almost 2,300 species are members of the rodent family. They range over every habitat (except the sea). They can be found on the ground, up trees and also in the water.

Rodents are clearly identifiable by their teeth: these include a single pair of large, powerful, curved incisors which form an arch, and each pair is situated in the upper and lower jaws. The incisors have no roots and continue to grow over the animal's lifetime. Canine teeth are completely non-existent in rodents. There is a gap between the back molars and the incisors. Rodents mainly feed on plant material such as roots, fruits and bark, but they also eat small animals. At the onset of winter, many rodents retreat to their burrows.

Rodents have especially acute senses of smell and hearing, which are better developed than their other senses. The reproduction rate amongst rodents is quite high. The gestation period is usually very short. Rodents can live between 1.5 and 18 years of age.

Humans use some rodents for their fur (chinchilla, coypu and muskrat), whilst others are used for research. Many rodents can be pests and carriers of disease. Lagomorphs (rabbits and hares) are fairly closely related to rodents, with about 80 species worldwide. Originally not native to Australia, Madagascar and New Zealand, humans contributed to their spread to these countries. In contrast to rodents, rabbits and hares have two pairs of incisors located in their upper jaw, which are therefore also called double teeth. This is why lagomorphs were categorised separately from rodents, so that they have their own mammalian order.

Mouse & rat family

The superfamily of mice and rats (muroids) is the most widespread group of rodents, with about 1,300 species in over 280 genera. Most species are native to tropical countries (Southeast Asia, Australia, Africa). In temperate zones, only a few are native species, to which rats, field mice, wood mice, house mice and harvest mice belong.

Mice mainly live in attics, gardens and fields. Rats frequently inhabit cellars, sewers and landfill sites. The diet of a muroid is mostly plant-based. These animals primarily become active at night, when they nibble on all kinds of edible material. This is how house mice cause considerable damage to foodstuffs. As they are the most fertile mammals in the world, a large number of young are born

Field mouse
Range: **Northern Europe to Central Asia**
Habitat: **fields and forest edges**

every few weeks, which become sexually mature themselves fairly quickly. The fertility of mice can even be found documented in the Bible: hence, large plagues of mice were considered to be a punishment from God.

House mouse

Range:
worldwide
Habitat:
open country near human habitation

House mouse

Wherever people live, the house mouse can also be found. With the grey coat and partially hairless ears, it looks really cute. The snout is fairly pointed. Whiskers are located in the upper lip area.

Furthermore, the long tail, studded with horny scales, differs from the much shorter tail of the field mouse. The house mouse can grow up to 24 cm long (including the tail).

Despite their rather cute appearance, house mice startle people momentarily when they suddenly shoot through the kitchen, for example. House mice inhabit all areas of the home and outbuildings. They use every nook and cranny as shelter. They go out foraging from these hiding-places and are mostly active at night. Then every so often the patter of feet can be heard coming from the attic or a rustling of paper, when they are eating something. As the house mouse is a nocturnal animal, or rather an animal that ventures out at dusk, it has good eyesight and acute hearing.

The house mouse's sense of smell comes into its own when it searches for food, as it gnaws through floors and doors to reach human provisions. It eats anything edible. Of course, sweet dishes, cheese and fruits are amongst the house mouse's favourite food. Moreover, if it picks up the scent, the house mouse nibbles on the same door each night— undeterred— until it has finally gnawed right through it. It drags particularly delicious items into its hiding place, where the house mouse hoards its supplies.

House mice are skilful climbers, using sharp claws that are attached to their four dainty feet as well as their long tail to help them. They race across the floor at lightning speed, without having first looked around to see if danger threatens. Then they crouch once more, before continuing to jump or running back into their hiding place.

Mice can swim too. However, they only take to the water in an extreme emergency.

Mice reproduce exceptionally quickly. Just 22–24 days after mating, the female gives birth to a litter of 4–8 young five to six times a year. The tiny baby rats initially remain in a nest, which is constructed of paper, bits of clothing or similar. They mature quickly. Each family of mice has its own territory. Unfamiliar intruders are driven away or killed. They can easily be recognized by their scent.

The house mouse's worst enemy is the cat. Owls also help to catch mice in old buildings, whereas in rural areas polecats and hedgehogs do as well. People try to control mice with traps or poison. The field mouse, wood mouse and harvest mouse are all related to the house mouse.

Rats

Rats are altogether larger than mice. They grow to over 30 cm in length and differ from mice in their habits.

The **Black Rat** has been native to Europe for some time now. It was mentioned by name for the first time in the 12th century. Its origin lies in Asia. Black rats grow to 20 cm in length and their tail can also reach this size. The coat is a blackish colour and the belly is somewhat lighter.

Brown rat

Range: **worldwide**
Habitat: **near human habitation**

The black rat had dominated in Europe until the 18th century, but then the **Brown Rat** gained ground there. Since then, brown rats have been in the majority, and they are slightly larger than black rats. Brown rats probably originate from Central Asia, from where they are said to have migrated in large numbers after an earthquake in 1727. Shortly afterwards, they migrated on the shipping routes from the East Indies to England and multiplied at an extremely fast rate everywhere. Brown rats have a greyish-brown to yellowish-brown coat on the top part of their body and tail, whilst the lower part is a grey-white colour. Whereas black rats are more likely to be found in granaries, barns or attics, brown rats prefer to live in sewers, damp cellars, on riverbanks and in landfill sites and so forth.

Brown rats live in groups. They are considered to be the carriers of epidemics. They eat practically anything edible. They especially like rotting carrion, but they are also not averse to grains and bark. Anything brown rats cannot eat, they nevertheless reduce to small pieces by nibbling away at it.

Rats are good swimmers and therefore easily managed to board ships as well, which is relevant to their rapid spread. Brown rats are also excellent divers. Rats have even been known to snatch ducklings from below the surface of the water as they swim across it, and then eat them. In addition, a rat's ability to climb is superb. Even almost flat walls are not insurmountable obstacles for them. Brown rats are more fertile than golden hamsters. Each pair of rats produces a litter of about 20 young every 45 days, which are sexually mature themselves after 10–12 weeks.

Capybara

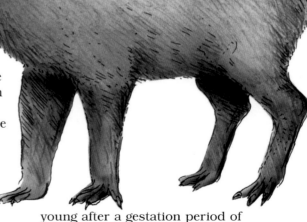

Capybara

Range: **Panama to eastern Argentina**
Habitat: **forest, close to water**

The cavy family comprises guinea pigs, pampas hares (maras) and the water cavy (capybara). The capybara is the largest living rodent in the world. At a metre in length and weighing as much as about 50 kg, it looks very inelegant. The build and bristly coat of the capybara is actually reminiscent of our domestic pigs.

The capybara can be found in forests close to water and marshlands in South America, where it spends most of the day in the water. It can swim and dive well. Its feet are partially webbed. Capybaras feed on land-based plants and aquatic plants, and therefore their back molars wear down considerably. However, they continue to grow over the animal's lifetime, which makes up for the extensive wear and tear.

Capybaras are primarily active early in the morning and in the evening. If the animals are disturbed, they only go in search of food at night.

Male and female capybaras are about the same size and look identical. The male has a larger scent gland on its nose than the female.

They prefer to be in the company of other capybaras. They mate in spring and the female gives birth to two well-developed young after a gestation period of 16–18 weeks.

Squirrels

Squirrels are rodents and are found throughout the world, with the exception of Australia. The Latin word for squirrel (Sciurus) means 'shadow-tailed'. The squirrel family comprises about 280 species: a distinction can be made between ground squirrels, callosciurus (also referred to as 'the beautiful squirrels'), tree squirrels and flying squirrels.

Ground squirrels mostly have a squirrel-like or hamster-like appearance. They are social animals and live together in large groups. The much larger marmots belong to the various species of ground squirrel. Marmots have a squat body and various species of marmot can be found in North America, Asia, the Carpathians and the Alps. Prairie dogs, which are native to North America, are also a type of ground squirrel, and live there in huge colonies.

Comprising about 35 species, the **Tree Squirrels** can be found in large parts of Asia, Europe and mainly in North and South America. These animals are skilful climbers. As tree-dwellers, they live in hollow trunks or build their

Ground squirrel
Range:
North America, Asia and Africa
Habitat:
grassland and scrubland

nests from moss and small twigs.

In colder and temperate zones, they hoard large quantities of nuts, cones and so forth, in preparation for the cold season. For the most part, they sleep through the winter. They only occasionally wake up to feed on their provisions. A typical tree squirrel is our **red squirrel**.

The **Flying Squirrel** is found in Asia, North America, Scandinavia and Siberia. The flying membrane sets the flying squirrel apart, and it is spread out between their front and back legs in flight.

Red squirrel

As it is a type of squirrel, the red squirrel belongs to the large group of rodents. This species of tree squirrel lives in Europe and in large parts of Asia. At about 20–24 cm in length, it has a large snout and big eyes, with which it can even distinguish between different colours. The coat is brown and soft, whilst the tail – which is 15–20 cm in length – is very bushy. The red squirrel is a lively creature that races through the trees at great speed. Its main

diet consists of pine cones, mushrooms, nuts and fruits. Red squirrels build their nest from twigs and moss; these are called dreys. They drag a supply of food to the nest during the summer, because they hibernate there during the winter, waking up occasionally to tuck into the food. The young are also born in tree nests. Depending on the climate, two litters of about

three young at a time can be raised within a year.

At the beginning of the last century, the grey squirrel was introduced from North America to England, to live alongside the red squirrel. Up to that point, the red squirrel was the only European species of squirrel.

Red squirrel (skeleton)

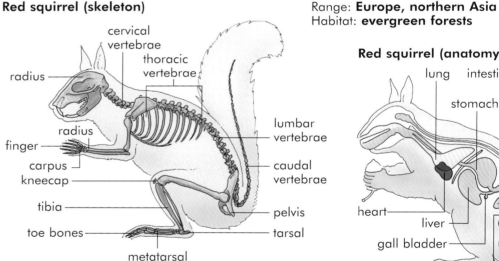

cervical vertebrae
thoracic vertebrae
radius
radius
finger
carpus
kneecap
tibia
toe bones
metatarsal
lumbar vertebrae
caudal vertebrae
pelvis
tarsal

Range: **Europe, northern Asia**
Habitat: **evergreen forests**

Red squirrel (anatomy)

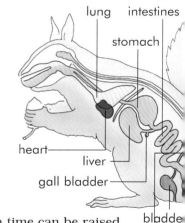

lung   intestines
stomach
heart
liver
gall bladder
bladder
kidney

Marmot

Like all marmots, the Alpine marmot also has a squat body. It grows to about 65 cm in length and 18 cm tall. The coat is very thick and consists of shorter downy hair and longer coarse hair.

The marmot's weight varies in accordance with the season. In autumn, they put on fat reserves in preparation for winter hibernation. Shortly before they hibernate, they can weigh up to 5.5 kg and by spring have lost 2 kg in weight. Marmots drag plant leftovers into the burrow for food before winter sets in, which they use as padding and warm insulation. At the onset of winter, the animals snuggle up together and fall into a state of suspended animation. If they have insufficient fat reserves, many marmots die, with young animals being

Marmot
Range: **North America, Asia, Carpathians and the Alps**
Habitat: **burrows**

particularly vulnerable. In spring, they often have to travel long distances in order to find the first tender shoots of grass once more.

The Alpine marmot loves the sun and digs out burrows, which is the reason it belongs to the ground squirrel family. One section of the burrows is small, simple and only intended for the summer months. Other sections are located deeper underground and are meant for the long hibernation. These larger burrows are lined with hay and grass and provide shelter for whole families of the marmots. They also contain small chambers for their droppings; these are situated next to their living quarters.

When digging, marmots loosen the sand with one of their front feet. When a small heap has accumulated, they push it out of the burrow with both of their back feet. They break up larger stones with

their teeth. In the meantime, marmots constantly come out of the burrow to shake off the loose earth from their coat.

Towards dawn, marmots look cautiously out of their burrows, venturing out tentatively, and immediately start eating grass and vegetation. They bite off various parts of plants with their sharp teeth, and hold them with their front paws whilst standing on their back legs. They only seldom drink water, but when they do they imbibe in great quantities. When marmots hear a noise, they utter a deep, loud whistle, to sound the alarm. Then they all disappear into their burrows as quick as a flash.

During the mating season in spring, the female marmot lines a corner of her burrow with grass. She remains there for five weeks, after which she gives birth to a litter of up to seven offspring. They are blind at birth and hairless, but after only a few days, a first coat starts to appear, which is very dark in colour. After about 40 days, the young leave the burrow for the first time and immediately head out to forage for food. At the end of the summer, the young and their parents have the same colour coat. They do not reach adult size until their second year.

Prairie dog

The prairie dog is another member of the ground squirrel family and lives in North America. It is much smaller than the marmot. The prairie dog did not acquire its name because of any similarity to dogs, but because in the past trappers named it after its bark, which it uses as a warning call.

Prairie dogs live together in huge social groups of hundreds of individuals, and even thousands.

These animals are stout-bodied and have a large head. The tail is short and bushy. The back is reddish brown, grey and black in

colour, whilst the underside is greyish white. Prairie dogs grow to about 40 cm in length (with a tail measuring 7 cm). They live in underground burrows. The dwellings ('wards') of individual family groups are interconnected by numerous systems of tunnels.

Prairie dogs only eat a specific type of grass and roots. Due to their prodigious spread, prairie dogs have been shot, poisoned and snared. Their numbers had declined in the last few centuries, but nowadays there are colonies with several thousand individuals once more.

Prairie dog
Range: **North America**
Habitat: **grassland and underground burrows**

51

Beaver

Beaver

Range: **North America, Europe, Asia**
Habitat: **rivers, lakes with shoreline vegetation**

Beavers live in large parts of Europe, North America and Canada. These animals, which grow up to a metre in length and can weigh up to 30 kg, are perfectly adapted to an aquatic life. Beavers use their front paws to grasp individual objects.

Their back legs are equipped with long webbed feet. Beavers have a broad, flat tail up to 30 cm long, which they use as a rudder in the water and when they stand on dry land it provides them with additional stability.

The beaver uses its powerful teeth to topple softwood poplars, willows and ash trees. However, they leave beech trees, oak trees and conifers alone. The beavers gnaw away at the trees situated upstream and near the riverbank to such an extent, that they fall into the water, and then they float them along to the lodge and the dam. If need be, trees that are further afield are also felled and transferred across water channels the beavers have built themselves. The beaver's diet mainly consists of aquatic plants and tree bark. However, it does not touch the wood it has used to construct the dam.

The beaver's lodge, which is constructed of intertwined trees and branches and is sealed with stones, parts of plants and mud, has an emergency exit at the top and several entrances beneath the surface of the water. Within the lodge, there is a platform above the water surface. After mating has taken place between January and March, between two and four beaver kits are born, after a gestation period of about 105 days. Beavers can live for 10–15 years. At the end of the 19th century, their population declined to such an extent, on account of intensive hunting, that these animals were placed under protection. In the meantime, beaver populations and their geographical range have recovered again.

Porcupine

Porcupine

Range: **Africa, Asia, Europe**
Habitat: **forest, savanna**

The porcupine is a member of the rodent family and not a member of the pig family, as the name might suggest. Five genera of porcupine are found in the warmer regions of Africa, Asia and Europe. The African species belong to the actual porcupine family, which are about the size of a badger. The **Crested Porcupine** lives in North Africa (excluding the Sahara), but also on Sicily and in southern Italy, where it is said to have been introduced as early as the time of the Romans. The **South African Porcupine (Cape Porcupine)** is native to the forests and savannas of Africa, from Senegal to South Africa.

The porcupine's body is covered with hairs, which are transformed into sharp quills and bristles. They are black and white in colour and mainly located on the rear section of the animal. These quills can reach up to 30 cm in length, under which shorter tail quills are located as well. In the past, these quills were used by the indigenous people as arrows. When threatened, porcupines raise their quills and then back towards their attacker, warding it off with their quills. If a porcupine comes into contact with its assailant, the quills penetrate deep into the body of the enemy. At the same time, the quills detach, because they only sit loosely, and their numerous small barbs are designed to become lodged in the victim. The tips of the quills on the porcupine's tail are an additional warning signal. They are hollow and emit a rattling noise.

However apart from humans (who hunt them for food), porcupines have very few enemies, because not many animals engage in a fight with them. From time to time, a ravenous lion or puma tries to catch a porcupine.

In general, the porcupine is a very timid, solitary animal, which lives in rock crevices or burrows it digs out, where it stays during the day. Porcupines are only active at night when they set out in search of food. They do not have particularly

52

well-developed eyesight, but instead their exceptionally good sense of smell helps them to find roots, tubers and fruits. Their hearing is so acute that they can even hear a ripe fruit drop. When they eat, porcupines use their front paws to hold their food. They often store twigs and fragments of bone in their burrow to gnaw on and nibble, which is how their teeth are kept at the right length, because they continue to grow over a rodent's lifetime. Porcupines do not eat meat. The African porcupine reproduces two to three times a year, although the females are ready to mate about every five weeks. When mating takes place, the female flattens herself against the ground and keeps the quills close to her body. This strategy prevents either partner from being injured. After a gestation period of about 100 days, a litter of two or three young ('porcupettes') are born with their eyes already open. At birth, the young porcupines have a bristly coat, but the quills are still soft. However, the quills harden within the next few hours. In order to avoid injury, the mother's teats are located on the side of her body, from which her offspring can suckle in the following weeks. After only a short time, the young also eat solid food occasionally. When caring for her young, the mother shows deep affection.

In addition to the genus of actual porcupines, there are the **Brush-Tailed Porcupine**, the **Philippine Porcupine**, the **Short-Tailed Porcupine (Stump-Tailed Porcupine)** and the **Long-Tailed Porcupine**. They are mainly distinguished from one another by the type of quills.

Rabbits and hares

Whilst our brown hare (European hare) mainly lives in fields, the considerably smaller wild rabbit prefers areas with small rocks or bushes, where it can always find a place to hide. Only one pair of rabbits lives in each burrow, consisting of deep underground tunnels, where they usually remain during the day. Rabbits leave the burrow at dusk when they can venture out in peace, but always with caution, in search of food.

Wild rabbit, male (anatomy)

kidney
caecum
heart
lung
liver
bladder
testicles

Wild rabbit (skeleton)

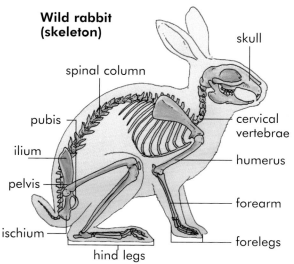

skull
spinal column
pubis
ilium
pelvis
ischium
cervical vertebrae
humerus
forearm
forelegs
hind legs

Brown hare (European hare)
Range: **Europe and Asia**
Habitat: **meadows and fields**

Long, powerful hind legs and elongated, narrow ears set the brown hare apart. Its coat consists of long coarse hair, which protects it from the wet and cold. It also has a warm undercoat, which is particularly thick in winter.

Wild rabbit
Range: **Europe and Asia**
Habitat: **meadows and fields**

From spring to autumn, wild rabbits can give birth to a litter of between four and twelve kits about every five weeks. The kits are laid in a chamber of the burrow, which the mother lines with some of the fur from her stomach area. The kits are blind for the first few days after birth. The rabbit mother suckles her young and seldom leaves them on their own, until she gives birth to her next litter.

Due to their fondness for tree bark, rabbits often destroy whole areas laid out for cultivation. Our domestic rabbits are descendants of wild rabbits. Particular breeds such as **Angora Rabbits** or **Silky Rex Rabbits** have an especially soft and velvety coat, which is used for delicate fabrics.

53

Primitive mammals

Marsupials rank among the most primitive of mammals. Although marsupials give birth to live young, the newborns are still dependent to such an extent, however, that they must continue their development in the mother's pouch for a few weeks before they can explore their world.

Most marsupials live in Australia nowadays. Originally, they could be found throughout the world, but then they were supplanted by modern mammals. Marsupials could only survive in South America, which was isolated for a long time, and in Australia where no mammals existed for a lengthy period.

Anteaters and sloths (the mammalian order Pilosa) are also primitive mammals. Most of them have a great many teeth, which often have no enamel or roots, however. In addition, their bone structure differs in part from the other species of mammals.

Furthermore, pangolins look similar to armadillos, which are related to anteaters and sloths. Pangolins also have scales to protect their skin, rather than a coat. There would be no point looking for teeth in these animals, as they have a long narrow tongue instead, which darts in and out of their mouth to hook their prey.

Marsupials

With 320 species, marsupials come in a wide variety of forms. However, they have one feature in common: their pouch.

In contrast to the more developed mammals, which are also called placental mammals, marsupials give birth to their young relatively soon after mating has taken place, in the early stages of their development. The tiny newborns (joeys) are not only furless, blind and deaf, but in addition have limbs that are not fully formed.

At this point, the embryos disappear into their mother's pouch of skin or skin fold. For the most part, they climb their way up into it by themselves. The pouch, which mainly opens to the front, is usually supported by two special epipubic bones (marsupial bones) attached

Kangaroo
Range: **Australia, New Guinea and Tasmania**
Habitat: **forest regions, scrubland and rocky areas**

Before the birth, the mother kangaroo licks the inside and outside of her pouch clean. The joeys develop for a few weeks in the safety of the pouch, before they grow so large that they can leave it. When they are born, the tiny joeys use their front legs to climb their way out of the genital opening of the mother into the pouch all by themselves, where they fasten onto one of the four teats and start feeding. Then the teats grow in accordance with the joey's rate of development.

56

to the pubis. The mammary glands are situated here in the brood pouch. The youngster fastens onto the teat and is nourished until it has developed fully. The joey leaves the pouch for the first time after several weeks or months, for short periods. However, it always returns to the pouch and also remains with its mother after it is fully grown, often up to the time when she is ready to mate again.

In the past, people believed that marsupials were originally native to Australia. However, nowadays researchers take the view that their true origin lies in East Asia, where the fossilized remains of marsupials were discovered dating back to the early Cretaceous period 125 million years ago. This was about the same time as the emergence of the first, more highly evolved mammals. As the continents were still joined together at that time, marsupials were able to cross over to South America and Australia. Marsupials were also found in Europe several million years ago. However, they were supplanted by the more highly evolved mammals.

Currently, marsupials are only found in South America (90 species) and Australia (230 species). They are divided into seven mammalian orders, with the animals reaching between ten centimetres and two metres in length, depending on which group they belong to.

Familiar members of the marsupial family are the koala, kangaroo, opossum and wombat.

Red kangaroo

ears

mouth

front legs

pouch

paws

tail

back legs

foot

sharp claws

Kangaroo

The kangaroo family, which consists of 65 species, is regarded as the most highly evolved of all marsupial families. They are the best-known animals in Australia. They are also found in New Guinea, Tasmania and the Bismarck Archipelago (group of islands). Some species are forest-dwellers, whilst others live in dry rocky areas.

The most striking aspect of kangaroos is the way they get around. With giant leaps, they hop along on their two back legs, which have large feet. The long and powerful tail helps the animal to balance when it lands on the ground.

The front legs, which are less powerful, have long curved claws. Kangaroos use them for the important matter of cleaning themselves.

Their bounding gait enables kangaroos to attain speeds of up to 25km/h. When they are threatened, they can even jump twice as fast over short distances. **Red Kangaroos** can jump seven metres long

Red kangaroo (skeleton)

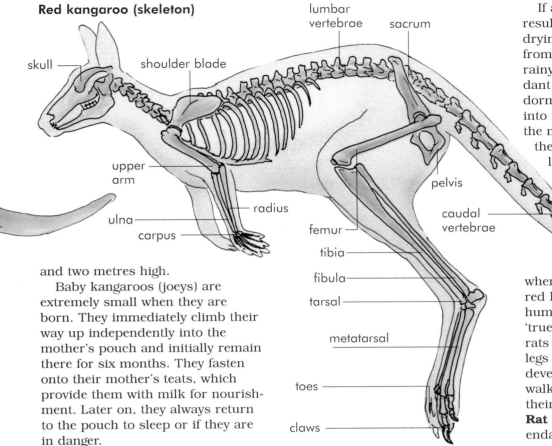

skull
shoulder blade
lumbar vertebrae
sacrum
upper arm
radius
ulna
carpus
femur
tibia
fibula
tarsal
metatarsal
toes
claws
pelvis
caudal vertebrae

and two metres high.

Baby kangaroos (joeys) are extremely small when they are born. They immediately climb their way up independently into the mother's pouch and initially remain there for six months. They fasten onto their mother's teats, which provide them with milk for nourishment. Later on, they always return to the pouch to sleep or if they are in danger.

If a prolonged period of drought results in the mother's milk supply drying up, she removes the joey from the pouch and it dies. In the rainy season, when there is abundant food once more, a so-called dormant or spare embryo crawls into the mother's womb, without the need for her to be fertilized by the male again. Therefore, there is little risk that kangaroos will become extinct.

The smallest kangaroo species called the **Nabarlek** is the size of a cat, whereas the red kangaroo grows to the size of a human. **Rat Kangaroos** differ from 'true kangaroos' and are the size of rats or domestic cats. Their back legs are considerably more poorly developed. Therefore, they mostly walk on all fours and only hop on their back legs when threatened. **Rat Kangaroos** are a critically endangered species.

Opossum Range: **North and South America**
Habitat: **forested regions and scrubland**

Opossum

The familiar North American possum is an opossum belonging to the mammalian order of marsupials. It lives in southeast Canada, Nicaragua as well as the USA, and is the largest opossum.

The animal can grow up to 50 cm in length and has a long, thick tail. Fur only covers the top of the tail, which is otherwise hairless. Opossums are tree-dwellers, because they are agile climbers. For this purpose, they mainly use their opposable thumb to help them grip and hang onto the branches. The prehensile tail also provides support when they are climbing. The animal can even hang upside down by its tail and remain in this position for hours.

Opossums eat everything they find. Primarily, they look for food on landfill sites and amongst discarded litter. If they feel threatened by a lynx or a dog, they pretend to be dead, until the enemy has disappeared again.

In Canada, the female gives birth once a year to up to 18 young, of which usually only between six and eight survive, however. In more southern regions it can even be three times a year. They develop in their mother's pouch. In the southern United States, possums are hunted for their fur, but also for their meat.

Koala

One of the best-known marsupials is the koala. It is a tree-dweller and lives in dry forests in eastern Australia. It only comes down to the ground to get to the next tree.

This teddy bear-like creature, which grows to 60–80 cm in length, feeds exclusively on the leaves of just a few species of eucalyptus trees. It is only seldom found in UK zoos, because these trees do not thrive here in abundance. An adult koala eats up to a kilogram of leaves every day.

Koalas are mainly solitary animals that only come together to mate. Some koalas also establish small groups which consist of one male and a few females.

After mating has taken place in the summer, a single offspring (joey) – rarely two – is born after a gestation period of just one month. This tiny creature weighs only half a gram at birth! Then it spends 6–8 months in the mother's pouch, which opens towards the rear. Later on, the joey is carried on its mother's back. After it has been weaned off her milk, it starts to eat leaves which are pre-digested by its mother.

An adult koala weighs about 15 kg, and therefore 30,000 times heavier than at birth. During the first 30 years of the 20th century, vast areas of forest were burnt down to make way for sheep farming. In the process, part of the koala's habitat was destroyed.

At the same time, the animals were killed for their soft silver-grey coat. Moreover, a sexually transmitted disease led to blindness and infertility in koalas. When their numbers had declined to a few thousand animals within the space of a few years, substantial protective measures helped to conserve the species. In some

regions, koala numbers are on the increase again.

Wombat (bare-nosed wombat)

Range: **Australia and Tasmania**
Habitat: **heathland and forests**

Wombats

Wombats are powerfully built marsupials that look somewhat similar to our badger. They are native to Australia and one species also lives in Tasmania (the bare-nosed wombat), where they inhabit heathland and forests.

A wombat has long claws, with which it digs systems of tunnels beneath the ground, excavating between and around tree roots, whilst looking for tubers and roots to eat, because wombats are herbivores (feed on just grass or plants). They often raid entire cereal fields. Therefore, wombats are very unpopular with farmers and have already been wiped out across large areas.

With a body length of up to 1.20 m, the bare-nosed wombat digs tunnels up to 15 m in length that can be 2 m deep.

A female wombat gives birth to a single offspring in autumn, which from then on remains in the mother's pouch for 3 months and suckles milk from two teats. Even when the joey has left the pouch, it stays for several months with its mother.

It is not precisely known whether wombats form groups underground or are entirely solitary animals. Bare-nosed wombats can live more than 20 years.

Anteaters, sloths, and armadillos

Anteaters and sloths (the mammalian order Pilosa), and their relatives the armadillos, are very primitive mammals that are found in South and Central America. A few species of Pilosa have no teeth, but a large number of them have up to 100 teeth, with no enamel or roots.

Whilst in former times some anteaters and sloths were the size of a rhinoceros, nowadays only individuals the size of a wolf can be found.

Anteaters, sloths and armadillos are also known as Xenarthra 'strange joints', because they have an additional joint between their thoracic vertebrae and lumbar vertebrae. A special feature is the structure of the pelvis, where all the bones that usually exist separately are fused together and also with the anterior caudal vertebrae and the sacrum.

Pangolins (scaly anteaters) are mammals native to Asia and tropical Africa. They look like armadillos, but their scales overlap like roof tiles or pine cones. The scales are relatively large, sharp and supple.

Pangolins are nocturnal animals. During the day, they sleep in trees or in burrows, which they also partly dig out themselves with the sharp claws on their forelegs.

They feed on termites and ants. They first open the nests with their front claws and then retrieve the insects by probing with their extremely long tongue.

Armadillo

The armadillo lives in South and Central America. As a relative of anteaters and sloths, it is an ungainly creature with a stocky, elongated body and large ears. It has a long, powerful tail and the legs are short with strong claws. The entire upper side of the armadillo as well as the head is encased in an armour-like skin. It consists of stripes which look like belts and are joined together by folds of skin. These banded rows set each of the different species apart. They can consist of four-sided or six-sided bony plates (called 'scutes') between which irregular bony plates are integrated.

Armadillos live on open plains and in fields. They are solitary animals. During the mating season, several of them gather together.

During the day, armadillos mostly burrow in underground tunnels, which cover a large area. Two species live underground all the time.

The burrow is usually found near anthills or termite mounds, because this is where they find their food, which includes spiders and small vertebrates. Armadillos generally move very slowly. But if danger threatens, they can burrow into the earth as quick as a flash.

These animals are not very popular amongst the inhabitants of South America. The ground is constantly caving in due to their system of tunnels, when settlers are out riding on horseback. This often results in injuries to horse and rider.

Armadillo

Range: **South and Central America**
Habitat: **fields, grassland and semi-desert**

Armadillos usually give birth to between two and four identical young (up to twelve, by way of exception). They can walk after one week and can see after 3–4 weeks. They are sexually mature themselves at the age of nine months.

An armadillo's size varies considerably from species to species. The so-called **Pichiciegos**, which live underground and only come to the surface at night, are about the size of a hamster. Both species are threatened with extinction.

The **Tolypeutes** can grow to about 40 cm long and roll up into a ball.

The body of the **Giant Armadillo** is one metre long with a tail measuring 60 cm in length. It is the largest species of armadillo. Its numbers are threatened. Armadillos can live between 12 and 16 years.

Sloths

Sloths are tree-dwellers and are members of the mammalian order Pilosa. They live in the jungles and forest regions of South and Central America. They really do deserve their name, because they sleep for most of the day, whilst hanging upside down from tree branches. The four limbs are positioned very close together, the body is curled up like a ball and the head is pressed against the chest. They can effortlessly grip branches with their long arms and large claws.

Sloths become active at dusk

when they slide along unhurriedly from branch to branch to feed on young shoots and fruits. They conserve water by licking off the dew from leaves.

The thick furry coat grows in the opposite direction to the hair of other mammals: from the belly to the back rather than the back to the belly, which enables the rain to run off easily.

A female sloth only has a single offspring, which is well developed at birth. It already has a thick coat and powerful claws and toes. At the same time, the offspring immediately clings to the mother's neck;

she then carries it around with her everywhere.

The **Two-Toed Sloth** with two toes on each front foot can be distinguished from the **Three-Toed Sloth** with three toes on each front foot. The three-toed sloth or **Unau** that lives in the north of South America grows to about 65 cm in length. The fur on its body is olive-grey; towards the back it is a little darker and somewhat more greenish on the head, neck and face. The three-toed sloth or **Ai** that lives in the northeast of South America grows to 60 cm in length. Its fur is reddish grey, with a more silver grey on the stomach.

Three-toed sloth

Range:
South America
Habitat:
primeval forests

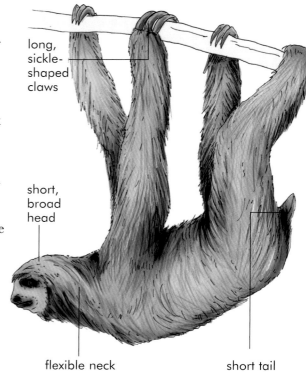

long, sickle-shaped claws

short, broad head

flexible neck

short tail

Three-toed sloth in a resting position

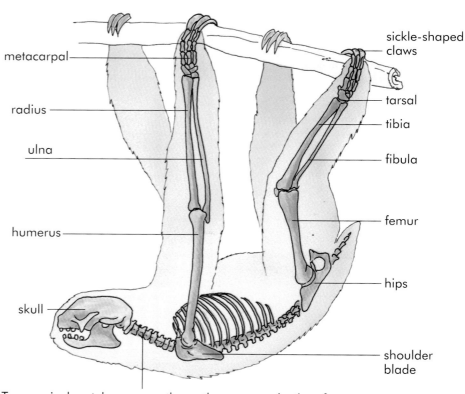

metacarpal

radius

ulna

humerus

skull

sickle-shaped claws

tarsal

tibia

fibula

femur

hips

shoulder blade

Two cervical vertebrae more than other mammals, therefore enabling them to turn their head some 270 degrees.

Three-toed sloth (skeleton) in a resting position

Anteater

Anteaters are members of the mammalian order Pilosa and live in Central and South America. These animals really are toothless.

The body of a **Giant Anteater** grows to 120 cm in length and its tail is 90 cm long. However, the **Pygmy Anteater** only reaches 16 cm in length and is a tree-dweller like the medium-sized **Tamandua**. Anteaters have an extended body with a highly elongated head and snout. They have coarse, grey-black fur and a long bushy tail, which is spread across the whole body when it sleeps.

An anteater only eats ants, termites and grubs. It uses the powerful claws on its front feet to tear open the very solid ant and termite nests. When the insects scuttle out, the anteater catches them with its worm-like, sticky tongue, which it can extend a long way. This process is repeated until no more ants or termites stream out of the mound or until the anteater is full.

Anteater

Range:
Central America, South America to northern Argentina
Habitat:
forest, savanna

Pangolins

The largest pangolin is the African **Giant Pangolin**. This slow-moving animal walks on all fours and also sometimes stands on its hind legs, by using its tail to balance. At the same time, the tail is used as a weapon.

Pangolins can deliver powerful blows with their tail, and also produce a foul-smelling fluid from their anal glands, chasing away many an enemy in this way. If the pangolin feels threatened, it can curl into a ball as well and is fully protected

Giant pangolin

Range: **Africa**
Habitat: **forest, savanna**

Pangolins are ground-dwelling nocturnal animals. Large and sharp-edged scales overlap each other like the scales of a pine cone. Pangolins can tear open nests with their powerful claws and then cram the food into their toothless mouth with the aid of their long tongue.

by its scales.

A female giant pangolin only gives birth to one offspring a year. She makes a nest underground where the young pangolin is born after a gestation period of five months. The scales are still very soft at birth, but harden after just two days. After only four weeks, the young pangolin rides on the top of the mother's tail and goes with her to search for food. After three months, the offspring is largely independent.

Pangolin (skeleton)

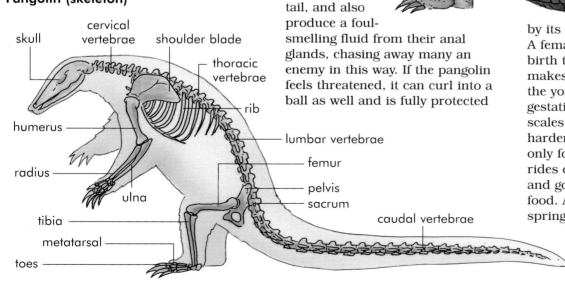

skull
cervical vertebrae
shoulder blade
thoracic vertebrae
rib
humerus
lumbar vertebrae
femur
radius
pelvis
sacrum
ulna
tibia
caudal vertebrae
metatarsal
toes

Odd-toed ungulates

With about 17 species, odd-toed ungulates, also known as odd-hoofed ungulates, are a mammalian order to which the horse, rhinoceros and tapir families belong.

Unlike even-toed ungulates, these animals have an uneven or unequal number of toes. Whilst horses, donkeys and zebras only have one hoof on each foot, rhinoceroses have three toes on each foot, both at the front and rear. Tapirs have four toes on their front feet and three toes on their back feet. With all of these animals, the middle toe is usually more pronounced than the neighbouring toes.

Alongside many horse breeds, donkeys, mules and zebras are also members of the horse family.

Horse family

The ancestors of present-day horses, zebras and donkeys lived as much as 50 million years ago. But at that time, these animals were only the size of a hare. They had not yet developed hooves, but had several toes, which they could spread wide apart. Therefore, they were able to move effortlessly over the marshy ground without sinking, in the warm and humid tropical climate at that time. Climatic changes

Mule
Range: **North Africa, southern Europe, China, South America**
Habitat: **sparse vegetation**

caused vast areas of the world to become arid. As a result, many species of horse became extinct. Other species evolved into the fast animals of the steppe.

About 3 million years ago, wild horses – which originally appeared in North America – spread throughout America, Asia, Europe and North Africa. Different species evolved that were adapted to the respective conditions. Wild horses gradually became extinct in Europe after the 8th century. The small Mongolian wild horse can still be found on the steppes of Central Asia today.

Horses have a slender frame and long legs. Their build is similar to that of the cow. Horses only have contact with the ground by means of a larger middle toe, which is surrounded by a powerful hoof. The other toes are absent or are considerably stunted. The elongated head

Range: **domesticated throughout the world**
Habitat: **grassland**

has large eyes, wide nostrils (nasal passages) and very flexible lips. The cone-shaped ears stand up at the slightest sound and can be moved back and forth. There is a mane around the neck. Horses have long hairs at the end of the short tail bone, which they swish to drive away horseflies or flies.

A horse's diet is purely plant-based. They mainly nibble at grass, which they shred thoroughly with their back teeth (molars), because they are not ruminants as are cows.

Male horses are called stallions and females are called mares. Mares typically give birth to a foal once a year.

Horse

Our domestic horse is descended from wild horses. It lived in herds on the steppes. Early on, it was used as a working animal and in addition it gained particular importance as a riding animal. The horse has a close, trusting relationship with humans, similar to that of a dog. It obeys when called, or through leg pressure when a rider wants it to move forward, and the horse can distinguish clearly between reprimand and praise. Horses still recognise their owners even after a few years.

As horses have been kept by humans, various breeds have evolved. Depending on the colour, a distinction is made between bays, black horses, chestnut horses, greys

Horse (skeleton)

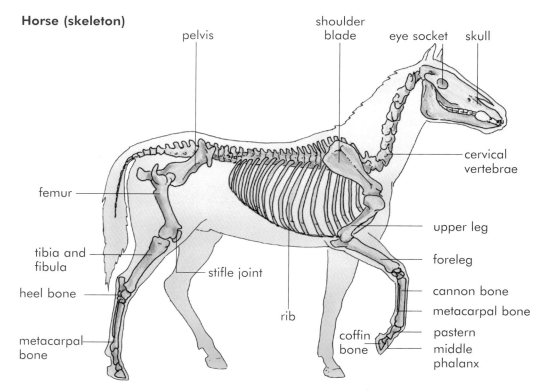

pelvis · shoulder blade · eye socket · skull · femur · cervical vertebrae · tibia and fibula · stifle joint · upper leg · heel bone · foreleg · rib · cannon bone · metacarpal bone · metacarpal bone · coffin bone · pastern · middle phalanx

and dapple greys. Ponies are particularly small horses. Depending on the temperament, horses are referred to as thoroughbreds, warm bloods and cold bloods (heavy draught horses). Like their ancestors that frequently had to flee from larger predators, domestic horses are also still highly sensitive to noise. This can be observed by their restless ear and tail movements. If a horse is provoked, it can even inflict a very painful bite or kick out with its hind legs. With anything unfamiliar, the animal 'bolts', meaning that it gallops uncontrollably from the scene. Horses have four gaits: the walk,

weight onto three legs in an alternating sequence, so that one leg rests each time.

Domestic horses eat oats, hay and grass, but also turnips, carrots and other vegetables. They use their lips to draw hay into their mouth, whilst they slice off grass with their incisors (in the upper and lower jaws). Horses have a caecum next to their stomach, in which a large part of digestion takes place.

The female horse – the mare – gives birth to a foal once a year. It is able to stand immediately after it has been born and accompanies its mother to pasture. Horses reach adulthood between the ages of two

Ass

Range:
north-east Africa
Habitat:
mountains, semi-desert, prairies

and three. Overall, horses have a life expectancy of up to almost 40 years.

Ass

The African wild ass, which is also called the true wild ass, is the ancestor of our domestic donkey.

Whilst our domestic donkey is regarded as stubborn, slow and self-willed, the African wild ass has a particular stamina and an agreeable nature, and is extremely undemanding, like its wild relative the Asiatic wild ass.

The African wild ass has a slender build. It stands about 1.20 m high at the shoulder. It has a large head with long narrow ears. The colour of its coat ranges from very light brown to grey.

It lives in north-east Africa in the mountains, in semi-deserts, on the prairies and in rocky areas, where it clambers about in search of grasses and other plants. Its favourite times to feed are at night and in the early morning. In the midday heat, it prefers to rest in a shady spot.

Adult male asses (jacks) are either solitary animals or live in separate small groups. The females and the foals of different ages establish loosely connected herds amongst themselves. If a dispute arises in their ranks, the animals start kicking and biting each other.

A female ass (a jenny) gives birth to a single foal after a gestation period of almost one year. She and her foal separate themselves from the herd, until the foal has learnt to distinguish its mother from others.

Horse, male (anatomy)

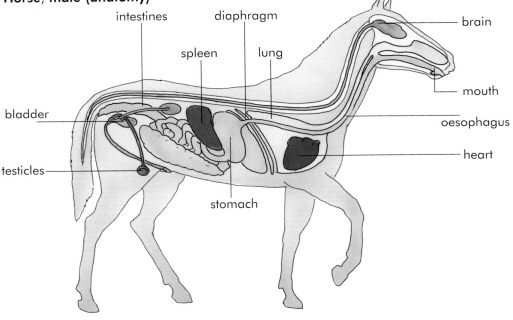

intestines · diaphragm · brain · spleen · lung · mouth · bladder · oesophagus · heart · testicles · stomach

trot, canter, and gallop. Whilst walking and trotting (the lengths of the strides are different), the horse puts down its legs alternating crosswise between legs (where the diagonal pairs of legs move forward at the same time). Then galloping comes about through a quick succession of leaps.

Unlike most other animals, a horse generally sleeps whilst standing. In the process, it transfers its

Gaits of the horse

walk

trot

canter

gallop

Zebra

Zebras are Africa's striped wild horses. There are three species with several subspecies. **Grevy's Zebra** is found in North-East Africa in ever-decreasing numbers. It has much narrower stripes than those of other zebras and its ears are larger. It grows to 1.60 m in height at the shoulder and weighs over 400 kg.

There are two subspecies of **Mountain Zebra**. After the **Cape**

Mountain Zebra was nearly wiped out, because it was reduced to 25 animals, it was designated a rigorously protected species. Today, their numbers have increased once more to about 1,500 individuals. Similarly, there are only some ten thousand individuals left of the other subspecies, the **Hartmann's Mountain Zebra**.

Nowadays, the **Plains Zebra** is the most widespread species of zebra, of which there are another five subspecies. Of particular note are the markings on the coat, which not only differ from subspecies to subspecies, but also from animal to animal.

The plains zebra is active as soon as day breaks. It moves from its resting place to grassland, where it eats grasses and plants. Occasionally, it visits a watering hole.

Plains zebras live together in large herds. A family group consists of about six mares and their foals, with an older stallion. If the stallion has reached a certain age (16–18 years), he surrenders his position in the herd voluntarily to a younger

Plains zebra
Range: **East and South Africa**
Habitat:
savanna and grassland

male, who must be at least six years old.

Even when many family groups are together in one herd, the animals can recognise their own group by the different markings, and the scent and snorts they produce.

Plains zebra mares give birth to a single foal after a gestation period of about a year. The mare and foal separate themselves from the herd for a few days. Once the foal has learnt to recognize its mother, they return to the others. The foal is suckled for about six months.

Tapir family

Tapirs are odd-toed ungulates. They are timid creatures that live in jungles and forest regions, avoiding open country.

They are about a metre in length and, with their elongated trunk-like snout, resemble wild boars. They have a stocky body and the sturdy feet have four toes on the front feet and three on the hind feet.

Tapirs mainly forage for food at night. They usually venture out alone and eat tree leaves and fallen fruits. Sometimes they invade orchards. In addition, tapirs are not averse to marsh plants and aquatic plants. As they are good swimmers,

tapirs are often found in water.

One species of tapir – the Malayan Tapir – is found in South

East Asia. This animal has striking black-and-white markings. The front part of the body and all four legs are black, whilst the back part is grey-white. There are four species in South and Central America, which are grey to dark brown.

Malayan tapir

Range: **South East Asia**
Habitat: **humid, marshy forests**

Rhinoceros family

Rhinoceroses are odd-toed ungulates and related to horses. These ungainly pachyderms have one or two horns on the bridge of their nose, which are situated one behind the other. The horns are constantly worn away and continue to grow over the animal's lifetime.

Dubious medicines have been made from their horns for thousands of years in Asia. As a result, these animals have almost become extinct there. It is a similar story in Africa.

Rhinos are found in regions with plenty of water, where they can rid themselves of troublesome midges and horseflies by wallowing in the mud. Rhinos often coat their skin with a thick layer of mud, by using their horns to churn up mud holes and then immersing themselves completely. At the same time, they make grunting noises as a sign of contentment.

At night, rhinos strike out into the nearby pastures and forests. In the process, they trample on every single twig, branch and bush with their powerful body, so that they leave behind proper rhino trails. They feed on all kinds of leaves, fruits and grasses.

A female rhino typically gives birth to a single offspring. She usually suckles it for a year and then keeps it with her for another two to three years.

The largest rhinoceros in Asia is the Indian Rhinoceros. This rhino grows to 4.2 m in length and looks armour-plated, because it has numerous dents in the skin.

The White Rhinoceros is the next-largest land mammal in Africa after the elephant. It is 2 m high at the

Black Rhinoceros

shoulder and up to 5 m long.

The Black Rhinoceros, also known as the **Hook-Lipped Rhinoceros**, also lives in Africa and grows up to 3.5 metres long. In contrast to the White Rhinoceros, it is mostly a solitary animal, and only the females stay together with their young.

White Rhinoceros Range: **southern Africa**
Habitat: **savanna and verdant regions**

Rhinoceroses love family life. They look after and suckle their young for about two years. Rhino young grow very quickly. After just one year, they have reached 2 m in length and a height of 1 m. They are a critically endangered species, because they are still being slaughtered by poachers for their horns, which are supposed to possess special powers. These animals can only be found in small areas south of the Sahara, in East and South Africa as well as in Nepal, Pakistan and Indonesia.

Even-toed ungulates

With over 230 species, even-toed ungulates, also known as even-hoofed (cloven-hoofed) ungulates, are mammals that can be found all over the world. The first even-toed ungulates lived as far back as 50 million years ago.

The distinguishing feature of this group is that they have one or two pairs of toes on each foot. The ends of their toes mainly consist of a material made of horn, the hoof. Most even-toed ungulates are animals that are able to run, eat plants and live together in herds. Tylopoda, ruminants, pigs and hippopotamuses belong to this mammalian order.

Ruminants

In the case of ruminants, a distinction is made between animals with antlers and animals with horns.

Antlers are horns that are extensions of the skull, which sit on bone structures and branch out with increasing age. They are shed once a year and replaced with new antlers. Ruminants with horns have structures made of horn tissue, which are supported by the frontal bone of the skull. The horns grow, but are not completely regenerated each year.

Characteristic of ruminants, such as the cow, is their stomach, which is sub-divided into four chambers: the rumen, the reticulum, the omasum and the abomasum. Food that is difficult to absorb is predigested with the help of bacteria, and then this material is initially regurgitated in small quantities, slowly chewed up and swallowed once more.

Non-ruminants

Non-ruminants only have a single-chambered stomach. These animals crush their food with their strong teeth.

Tylopoda

Out of the once numerous Tylopoda family, only the camelids survive today. In contrast to the even-toed ungulates, a footpad evolved from a springy, thick ball of fat.

Fallow deer
Range: **Europe, Asia Minor**
Habitat: **semi-open landscapes**

Roe deer
Range: **Europe to Asia Minor**
Habitat: **semi-open landscapes**

White-tailed deer
Range: **temperate climates of America**
Habitat: **forest, marshland, scrubland**

Deer family

Deer are ruminant, even-toed ungulates with antlers. They have a slender, graceful build. The head narrows towards the snout and is attached to a powerful neck. The legs are relatively long and the hooves are narrow and pointed.

The special feature of these herbivores is their antlers, which for the most part are only present in males. These constitute a pair of bony branching structures that extend out from the frontal bone of the skull. When the fawn is six to eight months old, it develops a bony platform on the frontal bone, which it retains throughout its life. This is called the 'pedicle', namely, the base from which the antler grows.

Red deer

multi-branched antlers

pedicle

slender, powerful build

thick mane around the neck (only in winter)

Range:
Europe, western Asia, north-west Africa

Habitat:
parkland, mountain regions, plains, moorland

narrow, pointed hooves

Deer foot

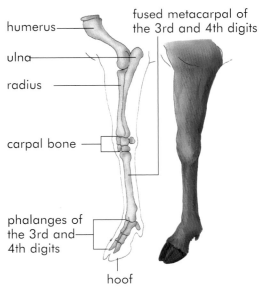

humerus

ulna

radius

carpal bone

phalanges of the 3rd and 4th digits

fused metacarpal of the 3rd and 4th digits

hoof

Initially, the pedicle is no more than a small pointed button on each side of the forehead, which gradually branches out more and more. Twelve shoots of this sort can form. Antlers are shed at the end of winter or in early spring and regrow in summer.

Males (stags) use their antlers as weapons in competitive battles for territory and for females. During the mating season, many stags bellow out their rutting cries, which are designed to impress not only the females but also their male rivals. The caribou, moose, reindeer and the European roe deer are members of the deer family.

Moose

The moose is the largest member of the deer family. An adult moose grows to 2.40–3.10 m in length and over 2 m in height at the shoulder, and weighs up to 800 kg.

The moose is easy to spot as it has a broad snout with a greatly overhanging upper lip, and a large flap of skin (dewlap) that hangs under its chin. The powerful paddle-shaped antlers of the male are equipped with numerous branches. They weigh about 20 kg. The moose has long, thick hair with a long mane at the top of the neck that continues to the breast and under the neck. The coat is reddish brown and is darker on the head and mane area.

During the mating season, the males (bulls) attempt to attract the smaller, antlerless females (cows) with their low bellowing. The bulls put up fierce resistance in the face of any rivals that appear on the scene.

After mating has taken place, a further eight months elapse before the moose cow gives birth to a single calf (only on rare occasions two). The calf is suckled by its mother for six months, after which it is able to eat plants as well. A calf stays with its mother for a total of one year.

With the exception of the mating season, moose are solitary animals and do not live in a group like the other species of deer. In summer, they mostly feed on aquatic plants and leaves. They eat woody plants such as bushes in winter.

Moose are found in every northern Eurasian country from Scandinavia to Siberia, as well as in Alaska, Canada and in the north of the USA, where they inhabit regions rich in forests and lakes.

Reindeer Range: **throughout the north of the northern hemisphere**
Habitat: **tundra and northern forests**

Moose
Range: **northern Europe, Siberia, Canada, Alaska**
Habitat: **coniferous forests next to rivers and lakes**

Reindeer

The reindeer or the caribou is the only species of deer where both males and females sport antlers, which have a unique structure. The lowest branch, that is to say the base of the antlers, has additional branches. The female's antlers are smaller than the male's.

The reindeer's body appears somewhat ungainly, with a length of between 1.2 and 2.2 m. It has a short tail measuring 10–20 cm and short legs.

Depending on the species, the reindeer's coat is black, brown, grey or white. Adult males are solitary animals, whilst the mothers and their young establish groups.

In summer, reindeer mostly feed on grass and other tundra plants. They search for mosses and lichens in winter. Reindeer frequently have to scrape away the snow with their hooves to find them.

A tame reindeer is the most important domestic animal for the Nordic pastoral nomads (the Sami). It provides them with milk, cheese and meat as sources of food, and bones and fur for their clothing. In addition, it can be used as a beast of burden and harnessed to a sledge.

Wild reindeer, which overall have a somewhat more delicate build, cover vast areas when they migrate with the herd in autumn and spring. Before the onset of winter, they move south, and they head north again in spring.

The males compete for the favours of the females in autumn. After mating has taken place and a gestation period of 240 days has elapsed, the female (cow) gives birth to a single calf, and sometimes two. Calves can travel with the herd within just a few hours of birth.

Reindeer are found in northern Europe and Asia, as well as in Canada, Greenland and Alaska.

Common tsessebe

Range: **sub-Saharan Africa**
Habitat: **open plains, grassland**

Springbok

Range: **southern Africa**
Habitat: **open terrain and treeless plains**

Gemsbok

Range: **southern Africa**
Habitat: **deserts and savannas**

Bovid family

The bovid family is a large group of even-toed ungulates. There are a total of 140 species, of which cattle, sheep and goats are the best known in the UK. The gnu, antelope and buffalo are also classified as even-toed ungulates.

This family of animals probably originated in Eurasia and reached North America from there. An especially rich variety is found in Africa.

One of the characteristics bovids have in common is the four-chambered stomach, which means that they are ruminants. During this process, the animal roughly chews up the food, which passes into the first chamber (the rumen) and then smaller quantities of food are subsequently passed into the second chamber (the reticulum). The food is pre-digested in the reticulum, where it now forms into small balls (of cud material) and is regurgitated, whereby it is then thoroughly chewed up (the cud) in the animal's mouth. After the animal has swallowed it again, the food reaches the omasum (the third chamber) and from there it passes into the fourth chamber (the abomasum).

For the most part, both male and female bovids carry horns. Female horns are usually smaller than those of the male. The horns are hollow, and have different shapes, depending on the species. They are used as weapons in conflicts between rival males.

Another characteristic of all bovids is that they only have the third and fourth toes on each foot, which have evolved into cloven hooves (two-hoofed toes).

Ruminant bovids usually live together peacefully in groups and feed exclusively on vegetation such as plant material, leaves, roots and so forth.

Cattle

For thousands of years, cattle have been the most useful domestic animals to humans, because they provide us with meat, milk and leather. As far back as the Stone Age, their ancestors – the aurochs (urus) and close relative the wisent – were hunted. At the time when the wisent was still in existence, the aurochs had been extinct for 400 years.

The behaviour of cattle is a strong reminder of their ancestry. Grazing cattle are social animals that live together in herds, in which a fixed hierarchy prevails. As the leader of the herd, one particular animal holds a special position. The others follow the leader in a fixed order. The higher-ranking animals also take the lead when returning to the cowshed and feeding station. They are permitted to eat before the other cattle. Cattle communicate with each other by mooing, grunting and bellowing. As cattle have a good mem-

Cow (anatomy)

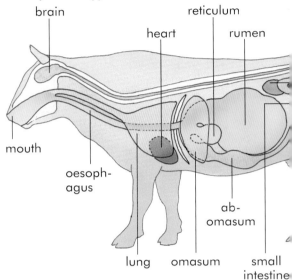

ory, they recognise the route to the pasture and follow the farmer's calls.

Cattle have a bulky frame. Their long tail has a tassel on the end which they use to ward off the ever-bothersome flies and horseflies. Cattle are bovids. Each horn is formed of a so-called horny sheath (of keratin), which surrounds the bony core, supported by the frontal bone, and is used as a weapon. The female, the cow, is more docile than the male (bull). A bull can be very dangerous to humans, when it angrily charges at someone.

Cattle are even-toed ungulates; they only walk on their two big toes (namely hooves split into two toes = cloven hooves), which correspond to our third and fourth toes. In the process, they only walk on the tips of their toes; that is to say, on the last digit, which is covered with a hoof. Therefore cattle are

Cow (skeleton)

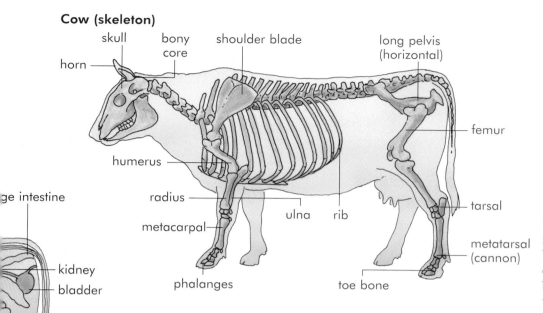

Cattle were bred by humans as long as 11,000 years ago and they have remained the most important domestic animals to this day, because they provide us with meat and milk. Their ancestors were the aurochs, which lived in small herds in the forests of Europe and in Asia.

digitigrades, like all hoofed animals. Another two toes that are stunted and do not touch the ground are situated next to each of these two powerful digits.

Cattle are exclusively herbivores. They are fed forage such as clover and grass. In addition, cattle eat hay, straw and turnips. Wherever possible, cattle are put out to graze. They wind their rough tongue round tufts of grass and draw them into their mouth.

Eight large protruding teeth, which are located in the lower jaw, press the tufts of grass against the gristly edge of the upper jaw and they strip the food off in this way. Cattle use their wide molars, which are situated further back in their mouth, to roughly shred their food in a sideways motion of the lower jaw before swallowing it.

Cattle can digest vegetation only if they grind it finely. Therefore they ruminate (chew the cud). To this end, cattle usually lie down in a comfortable position.

When cattle graze, the coarse parts of the vegetation initially pass into the first chamber of the stomach, the rumen (100 litres capacity), in which the process of

fermentation and softening takes place, lasting several hours.

Gradually, smaller quantities of food find their way into the second chamber of the stomach, the reticulum, after which they regurgitate the small balls of cud material. Then the cattle chew them up with plenty of saliva over a lengthy period. Afterwards, they swallow the food again and it passes across the rumen and reticulum into the third chamber, the omasum, where the fluid is extracted. The remaining fluid reaches the fourth chamber, the abomasum, where actual digestion takes place, as the food is broken down by digestive juices in the abomasum. Then the food pulp reaches the intestines, where the pancreas, gall bladder and intestinal juices complete the digestive process.

As a general rule, a cow gives birth to a single calf once a year. The calf can stand up immediately after it has been born and accompany its mother. Like all mammals, the calf is suckled by its mother. The cow's udder is used for this purpose, as it contains large mammary glands. The calf can suckle from the teats.

Due to continuing advancements in cattle breeding, nowadays a cow can yield far in excess of 7,000 litres of milk a year. Milk is a food for us which, besides water, contains valuable nutrients (protein, lactose, fat).

Range: **sub-Saharan Africa**
Habitat: **savanna, forested hill country and rocky terrain**

Range: **sub-Saharan Africa**
Habitat: **near water**

Range: **worldwide**
Habitat: **mountain pastures, meadows and grassland**

73

Hartebeest

Very different animals ranging from the size of a hare to that of a cow are members of the antelope family, which are classified as ruminant bovids.

For example, the **Hartebeest** lives on the prairies of sub-Saharan Africa, where it eats young shoots which have only just sprouted. They can often be seen grazing collectively with zebras or gazelles. Whenever the opportunity arises, they bathe in the mud.

Hartebeest drink a lot of water, but they can also survive without water for a long time without any difficulty. One of their favourite pursuits is licking salt.

Hartebeest have a light-brown or dark-brown coat. Males and females both sport horns, which are attached to their narrow head. The size and shape of the horns is different.

Hartebeest mostly live together in herds of up to 40 animals. Each herd consists of the females, their young and an alpha male, which guards the herd. Young males establish their own herds.

Females give birth to a single offspring after a gestation period of eight months. It remains with its mother for about three years, until it is assimilated into another herd.

Sheep

The flat forehead and the spiral-shaped horns, tilted at an angle, set sheep apart from goats. In addition, sheep do not have a beard.

Wild sheep live in the mountains of the northern hemisphere, and each geographical range has its own species. Originally from Asia, they have spread as far as southern Europe and North America in the interim.

The Barbary sheep is a wild sheep native to Africa. It can be distinguished from other species of sheep by its long mane, which is located on its chest and neck and also grows on its forelegs. It lives in rocky, dry regions and feeds on grasses, vegetation, twigs and leaves. This vegetation compensates for the lack of water, together with licking off the morning dew.

When they are threatened, Barbary sheep have little protection. However, they are well camouflaged by their grey-yellow to sandy-coloured coat. If they sense a predator is close by, they remain perfectly still and therefore can be overlooked.

Female Barbary sheep give birth to one or two lambs a year. The lambs roam with the female, male and lambs from previous litters.

Barbary sheep are hunted, because their meat and wool are

Domestic sheep
Distribution: **worldwide**
Habitat: **meadows and pastureland**

much in demand. As they are closely related to the goat, they are also called aoudad goats.

Domestic sheep mainly live on flat terrain. It is not precisely known when they were tamed. The European mouflon is probably an ancestor of the European (short-tailed) sheep.

Sheep are classified according to the quality of their fleece, and are bred as hair sheep, medium wool sheep, long or carpet wool sheep and fine wool sheep. A hundred years ago, the domestic sheep stock was considerably larger than today, because in addition to meat and milk these animals also provided wool and furs for clothing. Due to the rise in the manufacturing of cotton and synthetic fibres and because of the reduction in pastureland, sheep breeding has dramatically declined over the last few decades.

Hartebeest

Range: **sub-Saharan Africa**
Habitat:
steppe, prairie and scrubland

Goats

Various species of medium-sized bovids belong to the goat genus. For the most part, they are strong animals with a short neck. The horns are curved in different ways and are often pronounced.

Ibexes are true goats. The Alpine ibex lives mainly in the Swiss and Italian Alps at heights of up to 3,000 m. It only climbs further down the slopes in very cold winters.

The ibex has a grey-brown coat. All male ibexes have a small beard under their chin. Older animals also

Bezoar ibex

Range: **Greece, Asia Minor and the Near East, the Caucasus, western Asia**
Habitat: **mountains, hilly terrain**

have a long mane behind their neck. Males carry particularly striking long horns, which curve backwards. They are shorter in the females.

During the mating season, in winter, the nanny goats and the bucks are together. Males establish their own groups with the somewhat maturer young animals during the rest of the year, in which power struggles regularly take place.

In summer, the animals make their way onto the meadows of the high Alps where they eat the juicy plants and grasses. The young (kids) are also born at this time after a gestation period of six months.

Bison

The bison is a member of the bovid family and at one time lived in North America in huge numbers. Its population was estimated to have been about 25 million individuals around the year 1700. It provided the Native Americans who lived there with meat and furs for clothing and tents. In order to destroy the Native Americans, European immigrants tried to wipe out the bison, and by the year 1889 only a little over 800 animals survived. The bison was designated a protected species shortly before it became extinct, and today there are about 500,000 bison in existence once more, living in nature reserves in the USA and Canada.

These magnificent animals are about 2.90 m high at the shoulder. They have a powerful body with broad shoulders. Bison look very bulky in their thick dark-brown coat. The females are a little smaller. Young bison initially have a reddish-brown coat. Males (bulls) and females (cows) carry short, but sharp, horns.

Bison live in herds with the size of one family group reaching up to 1,000 animals. They eat grasses across the prairie and in the forests mainly in the morning and evening. They rest and ruminate (chew the cud) during the day, and at the same time they also like wallowing in the mud or the sand. This gets rid of the troublesome insects that constantly plague them.

Prior to mating, the bulls start fighting for the favours of the cows. After a gestation period of nine

Mountain goat
Range: **North America**
Habitat: **craggy mountains above the tree line**

months, a single calf is born away from the herd. The calf is able to return to the herd with its mother a few hours after birth. The calf is suckled for one year and remains with its mother until it has reached sexual maturity, which occurs when it is about three years old.

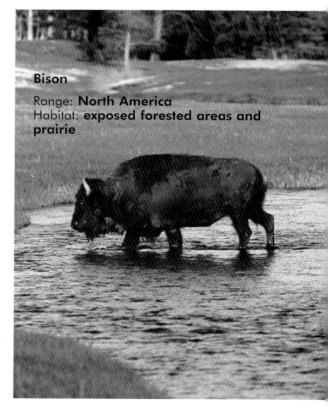

Bison

Range: **North America**
Habitat: **exposed forested areas and prairie**

Camel family

Tylopoda are even-toed ungulates. In the past, a wide variety of these animals existed and lived mainly in North America. Today, their descendents are the camelids, to which the dromedary, the Bactrian camel, llamas and vicuñas belong. Unlike other even-toed ungulates, they do not walk on the tips of their last big toes, but move forwards on both of their last big toes, the broad footpad which has evolved and connects these two long toes. This footpad consists of a thick, leathery layer of tissue, which is springy.

Guanako
Range: **South America**
Habitat: **semi-desert**

Dromedary

The one-humped camel or dromedary is used by nomadic tribes as a beast of burden and a mount for journeying across deserts. It has probably been kept as a domestic animal for as much as 6,000 years. It is also known as the 'ship of the desert'. It reaches a height of 2.30 m at the shoulder and can carry up to eight hundredweight.

In addition to the heavily built, load-carrying dromedaries are the long-legged dromedaries used as mounts, which can cover a distance of 140 km during the day. Both dromedaries have a short, shaggy coat, which is somewhat longer on the torso, behind the neck and around it. They feed on plants and vegetation, which they find in the desert. Reservoirs of fatty tissue (which can be broken down into water and energy) are stored in the hump on their back for when they cross long stretches of desert.

Even in the blazing heat, the dromedary can survive several days and even weeks without water. But to compensate it drinks more than 100 litres in one go, when the opportunity arises. It can manage for a long time with this amount of water, because it can increase its body temperature to about 40 °C. As a result, it does not sweat and loses less water in this way.

The dromedary has well-developed senses. It can detect the scent of an oasis even from a great distance. When a sandstorm is approaching, the animal becomes aware of it before a human does and picks up the pace, in order to find a safe place out of harm's way. The ambler has hooves with two toes, which have a broad footpad. Therefore it can effortlessly walk across the dry desert sand without sinking.

As dromedaries are protected by the thick, leathery tissue of their footpads, they are unaffected by the blazing heat of the desert sand or rough rocky terrain.

Dromedaries kneel down to rest or for the load to be removed. Here too camels are protected from injury by a leathery pad on the chest and knees.

Dromedary
Range:
North Africa, Near East
Habitat:
desert, semi-dry and dry grassland

Bactrian camel
Range: **Central and East Asia**
Habitat: **desert regions and steppes**

Dromedaries provide humans with milk, meat and fat. Tents are made from the skin and their dried dung is burnt for fuel.

Bactrian camel

In large areas of Central and East Asia, the two-humped camel or Bactrian camel takes the place of the dromedary. It is found in warm as well as in cold regions.

The most prominent feature of the Bactrian camel is its two humps. They have the function of a food store, because they contain fat, which the camel draws on when there is a shortage of food.

Furthermore, the thick, long and shaggy coat is a striking characteristic. It protects the animal from the winter cold. It sheds in summer and grows out in tufts, so that the animal looks shorn.

A Bactrian camel's body grows up to 3 m in length. Their tail is about 50 cm long. They feed mainly on leaves, which they strip from trees and bushes with their long incisors.

The female Bactrian camel gives birth to a single calf after a gestation period of 12–13 months. The calf can stand up by itself after just 24 hours. It is suckled for about a year and takes five years to reach adulthood.

Giraffe family

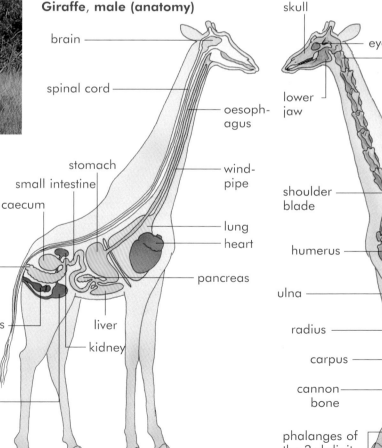

The giraffe family, which counts among the ruminants, was composed of numerous different species in the past. Only two survive today: namely the giraffe, which is found in sub-Saharan Africa, and the okapi, which lives in the rainforests of the Congo.

Giraffe
Range: **Africa**
Habitat: **bush and tree savanna**

The giraffe has a very long neck and grows up to 6 m high. However, the smaller animal, the okapi, only grows up to 2 m in height.

They both carry the blunt horns (ossicones) on their forehead, which are characteristic of the giraffe family. These are covered with skin and are not shed.

Depending on the region, the giraffe's coat is either quite light or quite dark and in each case it has even darker

patches of colour. In some giraffes, these patches are non-existent. The tail is about one metre long and has a tuft of hair at the tip.

Giraffes mostly live in small groups of six to ten animals and sometimes in herds as well. Each group consists of females and their young in addition to an alpha male.

Giraffes feed mainly on leaves, buds and fruits, which they pluck from the treetops. These animals find drinking very difficult: as they have long front legs, which are even longer than their neck, they have to spread their legs wide apart so that their head can reach the water. In general, giraffes eat early in the morning and in the afternoon. At

mid-day and at night, they sleep whilst lying down or standing.

Female giraffes give birth to a single calf after a gestation period of 400–460 days. The birth always takes place at sunrise! The calves are suckled for one year. They are already 1.50 m high at birth. However, it takes ten years for them to reach adulthood.

Okapi
Range: **Congo**
Habitat: **rainforest**

Giraffe, male (anatomy)

- brain
- spinal cord
- stomach
- small intestine
- caecum
- large intestine
- genitals
- bladder
- oesophagus
- windpipe
- lung
- heart
- pancreas
- liver
- kidney

Giraffe (skeleton)

- skull
- eye socket
- lower jaw
- shoulder blade
- humerus
- ulna
- radius
- carpus
- cannon bone
- phalanges of the 3rd digit
- cervical vertebrae
- rib
- pelvis
- caudal vertebrae
- knee-cap

Pig family

Wild boar

The pig family are even-toed ungulates and number almost 20 species, which live in Africa, Asia and Europe. Here, they are found in the forests, marshes and undergrowth.

Pigs have a stocky torso with an elongated head, which leads to a flexible snout with a flattened end. They use this sensitive snout to forage on the ground for food. Most pig species have canine teeth, which are referred to as tusks and grow out of their mouth. These are used when fighting an opponent and can inflict serious injuries.

Pigs are omnivores and eat roots, vegetation and mushrooms, but also insects, worms, mice and even carrion.

The wild boar and the warthog are members of the pig family. The domestic pig, which is the tamed form of the wild boar, is also a member of the pig family.

Range:
Europe, Central and South Asia, North Africa
Habitat:
dense deciduous and mixed forests

Domestic pig

The domestic pig is an even-toed ungulate and has been bred in China for some 10,000 years now. Studies have revealed that pig breeds were already said to have existed in Europe and the Near East at that time as well.

The origins of our domestic pig can be traced back to the wild boar.

However, in the process of domestication, it lost its dark bristly coat and other traits diminished as well.

The head became shorter, but higher. They evolved floppy ears, and a small hairless curly tail developed from the long tail with a tassel on the end.

The pig's short legs are very similar to those of a cow from the point of view of their structure – that is to say, pigs also walk on the tips of their toes. The second and third toes are greatly enlarged and are spread apart when the pig walks on marshy, soft ground. As a result, the smaller adjacent toes (outer two toes) also have contact with the ground and the pig does not sink into the mud.

Pigs feel most at home in a large run outside where they can wallow in the mud. After drying off, they like rubbing themselves against tree bark or wooden posts.

Formerly, pigs were driven out of their pen into the woods, where, as omnivores, they would use their elongated nose to forage on the ground for acorns and roots, but also for snails and worms and even for carrion. They were able to find food easily because of their excellent sense of smell and touch, located in the hairless tip of their snout.

A pig's teeth have adapted to its varied diet. Six incisors are located in both the upper and lower jaw. These teeth are almost horizontal and therefore form a vice, with which the pig can grasp even small morsels. Further back in its mouth, four sharp teeth in both the upper and lower jaws come first, and then three blunt molars. Therefore one section of its mouth suggests a carnivore, whilst the other section indicates a herbivore; pigs can reduce both meat and plants to very small pieces.

In the past, domestic pigs were fed with kitchen waste. In addition, they are fed potatoes, corn and milk.

Domestic pig
Range: **Europe, America, Asia**
Habitat: **forest, brushwood and undergrowth**

Warthog

Warthogs are native to Africa and have a cylindrical body with a sloping back. They are covered with a thick bristly coat. They carry a mane behind the neck and on the back, and sometimes these animals also have whitish cheek whiskers. The tail grows to 50 cm in length, and sports a tuft of hair at the tip.

Strange wart-like growths are located on both sides of the head, which give the animal its name. Two pairs of powerful tusks protrude from both sides of the mouth; they have formed from the canine teeth.

From morning to night, warthogs are out searching for food. In addition to grass and fruits, they eat tubers and roots, which they dig out of the ground with their tusks, particularly in times of intense drought. During the night and at the hottest time of the day, they retire to burrows to rest.

Warthogs enjoy wallowing in water, and therefore their territory – which they share with several family groups – must also be near a watering hole. At the same time, the animals use it as a drinking point.

Mating normally takes place during the rainy season. After a gestation period of about 170 days, the sow gives birth to between two and four piglets, which are then suckled for about four months.

Warthog

Range: **sub-Saharan Africa**
Habitat: **savanna and steppe terrain with watering holes**

Hippopotamus family

The hippopotamus is native to the water-rich regions of Central Africa. It has a huge body, which is about 4 m in length, and weighs up to 60 hundredweight.

The hippo is characterized by its dumpy, almost barrel-shaped body with the powerful head. Their eyes and ears are small. However, they have large slit-like nostrils.

The hippopotamus has an enormous mouth with especially powerful canine teeth – the tusks – which can grow up to 70 cm in length and weigh 4 kg. So the hippo scares its rivals by opening its mouth very wide and striking up a fearsome roar.

When a dispute concerns leadership of the herd or the best spots on the river bank, hippos engage in jaw-to-jaw sparring, by lunging at each other and fighting with sideward turns of the head.

Hippos live in herds of about 15 animals, which are led by one male.

Hippos are good swimmers. They have four webbed toes on the ends of their short, thick legs.

They spend much of the day in the water, where they also dive down to search for aquatic plants. They can remain underwater for up to six minutes.

When the animal wants to breathe, it only needs to raise its head a little out of the water, because the nostrils, eyes and ears are located on the same level high up on its face.

In addition to aquatic plants, hippos also eat grasses and fruits, which they find on the shore.

Mating takes place underwater, where baby hippos are also born. After a gestation period of 230–240 days, the female (cow) gives birth to her calf in shallow water. It is suckled for about one year.

When hippopotamuses lie down on the river bank to rest or bask in the sun, small oxpeckers – which are members of the starling family – and cattle egrets arrive, in order to rid the near hairless skin of leeches, ticks and so forth.

Hippopotamus

Range: **sub-Saharan Africa**
Habitat: **rivers and lakes**

Mammals with trunks

Mammals with trunks (Proboscidea order) are the largest living land animals. In the past, numerous species of these animals could be found across the whole world. These species included the mammoth, which became extinct long ago. Nowadays, only three species still exist, namely the Asian and African elephant and the African forest elephant.

Elephants are 4 m high at the shoulder and weigh almost 6,000 kg. which makes them the largest land animals. Their thick, pillar-like legs have a broad tread, which is composed of a tough, fatty tissue.

Their distinctive features are the large head with enormous ears, the upper incisors which develop into tusks, and the elongation of the nose and upper lip combined to form a trunk.

The elephant's trunk has many different functions. It uses the so-called finger-like extension to grasp objects. Furthermore, the elephant can use its sensitive trunk for drinking, eating and smelling, and also as a weapon.

Elephants are herbivores and live together in herds in the savannas, steppes and forests. They can live up to 60 years of age.

Asian elephant

The Asian elephant is a member of the Proboscidea mammalian order, together with the African elephant and African forest elephant. Their smaller ears and build distinguishes them from the African elephant. With a body length of 5.5–6 m, it can grow up to 3 m in height at the shoulder and weigh about 5 tons. As a rule, female elephants lack tusks. A finger-like extension at the tip of the trunk is used to grasp and investigate objects and food of all kinds.

The Asian elephant lives on the grass steppes and in the forests of India, South East Asia, Sumatra and Sri Lanka. Here too the elephants feed on grass, leaves and other plants.

The herds are led by an experienced female elephant (cow). With the exception of an older bull elephant, male elephants are unwelcome. Males usually establish their own herd nearby.

During the mating season, bull elephants secrete a strong-smelling fluid from glands located on either

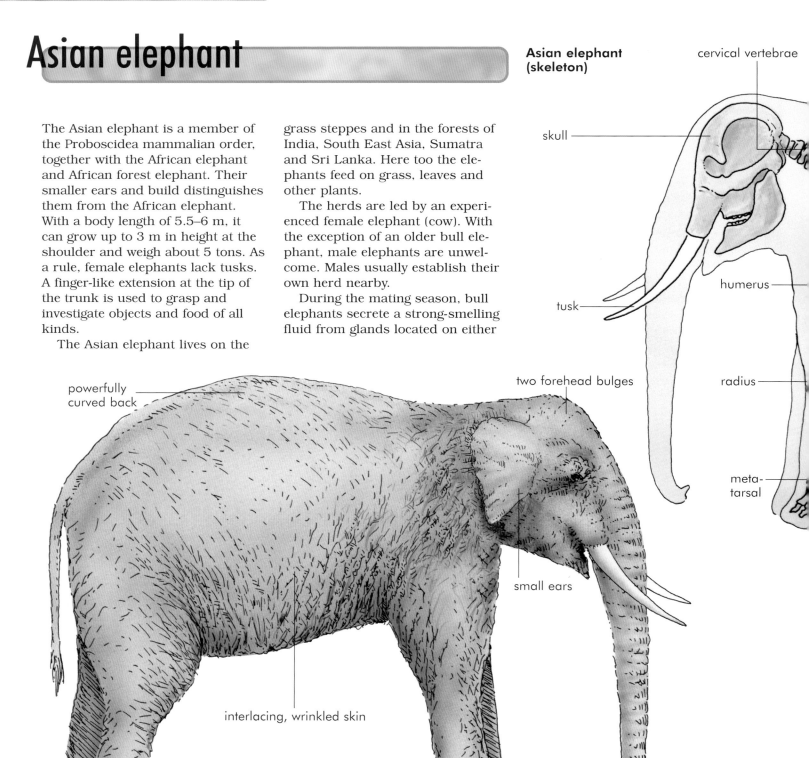

Asian elephant (skeleton)

cervical vertebrae

skull

tusk

humerus

radius

meta-tarsal

powerfully curved back

two forehead bulges

small ears

interlacing, wrinkled skin

only one finger-like extension

Asian elephant
Range: **South East Asia, India**
Habitat: **grass steppes and forests**

4 toenails

5 toenails

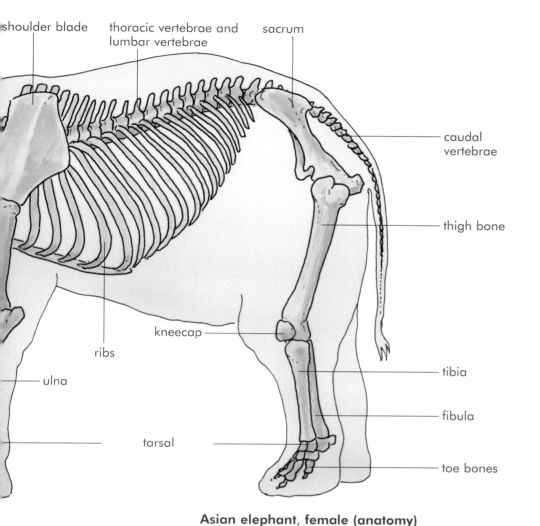

shoulder blade   thoracic vertebrae and lumbar vertebrae   sacrum

caudal vertebrae

thigh bone

kneecap

ribs

tibia

ulna

fibula

tarsal

toe bones

side of their head. The bulls are often unpredictable and aggressive at this time. After a gestation period of 21 months, the elephant cow gives birth to a calf. The calf is suckled for two years and also remains with its mother for a long time afterwards.

Unlike both its African relatives, Asian elephants are tamed for use as working animals. Their strength enables them to perform well, particularly with felling trees in mountainous terrain. In the course of this work, they are handled by so-called mahouts (elephant keepers). Elephants have been renowned for their capacity to work for at least 4,000 years. They were also used to wage war time and again. Consequently, elephants escorted General Hannibal and his army over the Alps in the war against the Romans.

As elephants rarely breed in captivity, wild elephant calves are often captured. They are trained from the age of 14, and from the age of 25 are also used for heavy work.

Asian elephant, female (anatomy)

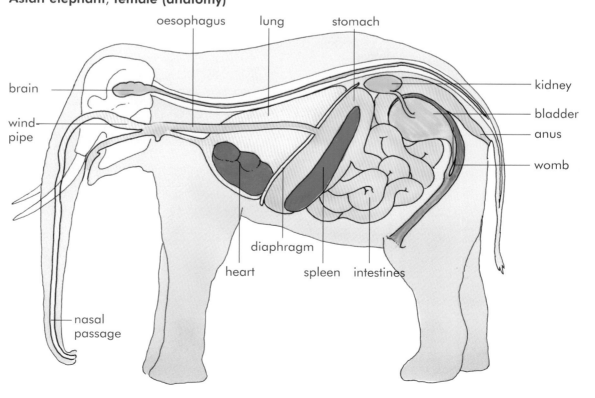

oesophagus   lung   stomach

brain

kidney

wind pipe

bladder

anus

womb

heart   diaphragm   spleen   intestines

nasal passage

Elephants walk on the tips of their toes. Asian elephants have five toes on their front feet and four at the back, whilst African elephants have four at the front and three at the back.
The individual toes are spread out and supported by a resilient cushion pad, which consists of fatty tissue and supple fibres, on which the bones rest. Externally, only the round, soft foot is visible and a kind of nail in the place where the toe ends. Therefore the bones are well protected and the elephant's weight is distributed over a larger surface area. Together with the resilient cushion pad, this gives these heavyweight animals their quiet and springy gait.

African elephant

The African elephant is the most powerful living land animal. It lives in the forests, savannas and river valleys of sub-Saharan Africa.

African elephants use their trunks to grasp leaves, twigs, fruits and roots. They tear them off and guide them into their mouth. However, elephants are hardly ever seen eating during the day as they prefer to rest, because they are active at night, in the morning and the evening. An elephant eats up to 300 kg of vegetation per day. In addition, it must drink over 100 litres of water.

The elephant's all-purpose organ, the trunk, is actually the extended upper lip. Therefore it also contains no bones, but is very muscular.

The trunk to an elephant is almost like the hand to a human. The muscles around the long nose give the trunk its immense flexibility. There are no rigid bones. The trunk is not only long enough to transport water or food from the ground to the mouth, but also to inspect the mouth of a partner.

They use the trunk to draw up water and then spray it into their mouth to drink. The trunk us used for trumpeting, picking up soil for dust-baths and smelling. For this purpose, the animals often stretch their trunk high into the air and sniff the air to detect water, food or danger. Moreover, elephants can grasp all kinds of things with a flap of skin at the tip of their trunk (the finger-like extension), such as tree foliage as well as the hand of a zoo-goer leaning too far over the parapet.

Apart from the trunk, the most striking feature is probably the ears. In African elephants, they are 1.5 m long. However, they are in fact used more as ventilation in the scorching heat and less to enhance their hearing. The ears are also attributed with the function of visual communication. By contrast, elephants have poor sight, because their eyes are small. Furthermore, the head is not very flexible, which makes their field of vision rather limited, despite the position of the eyes on the side of the head.

Bull elephants with a body length of 6–7.5 m grow up to 4 m high at the shoulder. They weigh up to 7.5 tons over their 30–40-year life span.

Both male and female elephants (bulls and cows) have tusks, although the females, which are of a smaller build than the males, have shorter ones. The tusks are deeply embedded in the skull and can grow up to 3.5 m in length. Out of the remaining teeth, only the first molar is used to chew tough vegetation. When it has worn down, the tooth behind, which has grown in at the back of the mouth, slides forward successively to replace it. If there are none left then the animal starves to death. Although it is hard to believe, these heavy giants tread really softly as they walk and are also quite quick, as they can reach speeds of up to 40 km/h if attacked. However, roaming elephants walk barely faster than brisk pedestrians. At the same time, elephants mostly walk in single file. They walk on the tips of their toes in a similar way to ungulates (hoofed animals); elephant toes have a thick, springy cushion pad. Elephants are incapable of jumping and therefore they can only walk through ditches or must remain on the side they find themselves. However, they swim across rivers and lakes and the water even helps to carry their weight. Elephants prefer to live in herds. Most herds consist of family groups, in which all the animals are related to each other. The oldest female is the leader of the herd and the other females and young elephants have a subordinate role to play. Some bull elephants also move with the group, whilst others are solitary animals or establish separate groups.

African elephant
Range: **sub-Saharan Africa**
Habitat: **forest and savanna**

Elephants do not reach sexual maturity until they are 15–16 years of age. A couple separates from the herd to mate. The elephant cow first prepares and lines a hiding place and then after a gestation period of 22 months she gives birth to a single calf in there. The calf can follow the herd after a few days and is suckled for five years. The calf finds protection within the herd, if a lion or a leopard has selected it as a meal. Apart from humans, elephant calves have no other enemies.

Humans hunted elephants for their ivory so intensively that these animals were only able to survive in reserves. In the meantime, their numbers have increased again to such an extent that they wander into the surrounding grassland and arable regions, where they are nonetheless persecuted once more, as vermin.

The enormous African elephant can be distinguished from the Asian elephant by its powerful ears and tusks. It has two 'fingers' at the end of the trunk, which it uses to grip plants, in order to guide them into its mouth. In this way, it takes in up to 300 kg of plant-based nutrition a day.

Marine mammals

Without exception, all present-day marine mammals are descendants of land animals. The oldest marine mammals are probably the whales. With their fish-like shape and the transformation of their forelimbs into fins, they have already become the best adapted to life in the oceans.

This is also true of manatees, which share ancestry with the elephant. Only seals, which are related to bears, can still manage to waddle across land on their flippers, to a greater or lesser extent. Seals (the three families of pinnipeds – seals, sea lions and walruses) are also the only marine mammals that need to come ashore to give birth to their young. Manatees and whales give birth underwater.

Whales undertake long migrations to warm seas to give birth, although they find most of their food in cold waters. But the temperature of the newborns would quickly drop too low in cold water and then they would freeze to death.

The reason why not only predators (seals and toothed whales) and plankton-eaters (baleen whales) but also vegetarians (manatees) are classified as marine mammals is explained by their different ancestry.

However, some adaptations for an aquatic environment are common to all: the hairy coat is often diminished or has disappeared completely, because the effect of the air trapped between the hairs on land does not exist in the water. A thick layer of blubber protects against cooling down, which made whales especially prized as prey by hunters.

In addition, it is possible for a whale's huge bulk to move only through the water, because only it can bear the animal's weight of several tons. If they become stranded on the shore, they are crushed to death by their own body weight.

Harbour porpoise
Range: **oceans of the northern hemisphere**
Habitat: **coasts, bays, rivers**

Bottlenose dolphin
Range: **seas around the world, except for polar regions**
Habitat: **coastal waters**

Dolphin
Range: **seas around the world, except for polar regions**
Habitat: **coastal waters**

Whales

Whales are mammals that live exclusively in water. They have a fish-like shape, which is adapted to swimming and they are often enormous. Depending on the species, their size varies between 2 and 34 m. They weigh between 35 kg and 140 tons.

Whales have a huge, hairless body, which has no visible outward structure at all and merges into a large head. The head consists of a mouth without lips and contains either numerous teeth (toothed whales) or baleen plates (baleen whales).

Whales have fin-like forelimbs, whilst the rear limbs have disappeared. They use the tail to move along in the water, which in contrast to fish is horizontal. The tail enables them to surface and submerge when catching prey at various depths. Whales are very good swimmers, and in the case of the sperm whale, dive up to 2,000 m deep. A thick layer of blubber is often situated under the skin, which insulates the animal's body from heat loss.

Whales have very small eyes, which lack inner eyelids. They can communicate with each other by producing numerous sounds, which partly lie in the ultrasonic range. Also, whales locate undersea rocks or shoals of fish with the help of ultrasound.

The nose, with its uppermost opening right on top of the head, functions as a blowhole. This runs through the nasal cavity directly into the larynx. From here, it is connected to a wide windpipe, which leads to a large lung. When it surfaces, the whale discharges spent air from this nasal passage, which is visible as jets of vapour several metres high. Whales swimming at a

Size comparison of whales

blue whale (34 m)

bowhead whale (18 m)

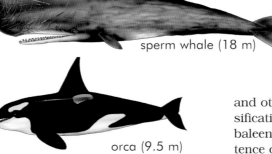
sperm whale (18 m)

orca (9.5 m)

pilot whale (8 m)

dolphin (4 m)

harbour porpoise (2 m)

steady pace breathe in and out about every one and a half minutes, but some whales also hold their breath for over one hour underwater.

An adult whale's diet is very varied. Whilst baleen whales feed mainly on plankton and small animals, toothed whales hunt seals, fish and other marine animals. The classification for toothed whales and baleen whales is based on the existence of either teeth or baleen plates (filter-feeder system), respectively, in the mouth.

Dolphins

The dolphin family, which are classified as toothed whales, number 40 species in total. They are found in every ocean as well as in tropical rivers. These mammals live permanently in the water, and breathe with lungs.

With their streamlined body and beak-shaped mouth, they rank among the smallest cetacean mammals (includes whales, dolphins and porpoises). Some relatives of this family look entirely different, as they are much larger, namely the killer whale (orca) and also the pilot whale.

Dolphins are fast swimmers. Their diet consists of fish, crustaceans, squid and so forth, which they mainly find close to the surface of the water. In the process, they come up to the surface to breathe several times a minute.

With the help of ultrasonic sounds, dolphins can navigate underwater. These sounds bounce off obstacles, but also off their prey (echolocation).

The bottlenose dolphin is one of the best-known dolphins, because it is found in every ocean of the world (except for polar regions).

Dolphins are highly intelligent animals that live in every ocean of the world and a number of tropical rivers. With their strong sense of cooperation, they also come to the rescue of their wounded fellow dolphins. If a dolphin is injured by a ship's propeller and sinks to the bottom of the sea, it would suffocate if it were not to swim to the surface to breathe within a few minutes. Just as dolphin calves are brought to the surface to take their first breath, an injured animal is also carried up to the surface by its comrades.

Dolphin (skeleton)

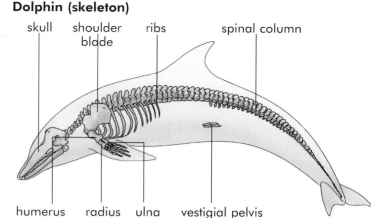

skull · shoulder blade · ribs · spinal column · humerus · radius · ulna · vestigial pelvis

Dolphin, male (anatomy)

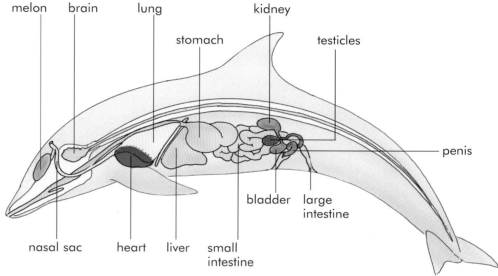

melon · brain · lung · kidney · stomach · testicles · penis · bladder · large intestine · small intestine · liver · heart · nasal sac

Killer whale (orca)

The killer whale, also known as the orca, is the largest member of the dolphin family, and is also classified as a toothed whale. It lives in the colder seas of this world and prefers coastal waters.

This powerful, streamlined animal grows up to 9.5 m long. Yet in male orcas, the dorsal fin alone can be as much as 2 m high. It is smaller in the females.

Killer whales live in family groups (pods) and also hunt together as a team. Although they have no established migratory routes, they nevertheless cover vast distances in the search for food.

Equipped with 40–50 razor-sharp teeth, they hunt fish, sea lions, and even other whales.

Killer whales use echolocation to track down animals in the murky waters, but the sounds they produce differ greatly from those made by other members of the dolphin family.

Killer whale (orca)

Range: **in colder seas**
Habitat: **coastal waters**

Sperm whale

Sperm whale

The sperm whale is the largest species of toothed whale (mammalian suborder). Its enormous head alone constitutes one-third of its body length, which measures between 10 and 20 metres. It has a very narrow lower jaw, which is supported from above and set far back. Sperm whales use their long, powerful tail to move along in the water and the pectoral fins are very short.

They can dive over 2,000 m deep, which is made possible by a special feature of the sperm whale: a waxy, liquid substance is located in a cavity above the toothless upper jaw, and is called spermaceti or sperm whale oil. It is said to help the whale dive to such great depths.

When tracking down prey in the gloom of the ocean depths, the sperm whale is aided by an ultra-sound system. They mainly eat squid, crustaceans and other marine animals.

In spring, all sperm whales migrate towards the poles, and then back towards the temperate waters of the equator in autumn. The females and their young remain in the temperate zones.

Range: **oceans and seas around the world**
Habitat: **temperate and tropical waters**

Male sperm whales fight to establish harems in tropical waters, which consist of 20–30 fertile females and their young. Males under 25 years of age form their own groups (pods).

After a gestation period of 14–16 months, females give birth to a single calf with the assistance of other sperm whales. The calf is immediately brought up to the surface by the female helpers, where it takes its first breath. Young sperm whales are suckled for a period of two years.

Blue whale

The blue whale, which is classified as a rorqual whale (baleen whale), is the largest living mammal that has ever existed. It is found in the oceans and seas around the world and reaches a length of up to 32 m, weighing 150 tons. Female blue whales are larger than the males.

These enormous animals live exclusively on small planktonic crustaceans (krill). In summer, they eat about 4,000 kg of this

Blue whale
Range: **oceans and seas around the world**
Habitat: **open sea**

food a day. During their migration back towards the temperate waters of the equator in autumn, they hardly eat at all. This is where mating takes place. The gestation period of the blue whale is 11–12 months, so that the calves are born in the warm waters near the equator.

The blue whale is also an endangered species, although they have been officially protected since 1967.

Humpback whale

The humpback whale is another species of rorqual whale. They live in the oceans around the world, but prefer to spend the summer in Arctic waters along the margin of the pack ice.

Humpback whales hunt in groups and surround their prey with a wall of air bubbles (a 'bubble net'). Then the whales stretch up their throat in powerful fashion and swim with their mouth open through the 'bubble net' into the shoals, close their mouth again except for a narrow slit to filter the food and force the water out through the baleen plates. The prey is caught inside and passes into the whale's stomach.

During the day, some fish shoals are almost 20 m long and weigh several tons. When they submerge, the whales typically arch their back into a hump shape. The tail has different shapes and in particular white markings, which makes it possible to distinguish between the animals.

Humpback whales can leap up to 15 m high out of the water. As this behaviour frequently occurs during the mating season and when the females give birth, many people have already been able to observe this spectacle, as the animals remain near islands and coasts at this time.

The courtship of a female can vary enormously. Some males pursue their chosen mate for days, whilst others try to attract the females by producing long and complex 'songs'. However, gory fights have also been observed.

The humpback whale became a protected species as far back as 1966, although whalers never hunted it as their primary source of prey. Nevertheless, whaling has severely depleted their numbers. Apart from humans, humpback whales are now only hunted by the killer whale. Currently, there are said to be about 11,000 humpback whales living in the Atlantic Ocean alone.

Humpback whale
Range: **southern and northern hemispheres**
Habitat: **polar seas and tropical waters**

Bowhead whale

The bowhead whale is a member of the right whale family (baleen whales) and lives in the Arctic Ocean. It grows to between 15 and 20 m in length.

It has an enormous head. The body narrows towards the tail. The bowhead whale has heavily arched jaws, which make room for the 4.5 m–long baleen plates. The baleen plates of the bowhead whale are the longest of any species of baleen whale.

The diet of bowhead whales consists of small krill which they catch through their baleen plates.

Bowhead whale
Range: **Arctic Ocean**
Habitat: **coastal waters**

Mating takes place in spring. In addition, the calves are born after a gestation period of 11–12 months and are suckled for one year.

The bowhead whale is now listed again as a vulnerable species. In particular, it was heavily persecuted in the 18th and 19th centuries. Nowadays there are several thousand individuals once more.

Harp seal
Range: **stretches of water in the northern hemisphere**
Habitat: **drift ice and ice floes in Arctic and subarctic waters**

Seals (pinnipeds)

With over 30 species, seals are the only group of predators that are semi-aquatic. This group includes the elephant seal, sea lion, walrus and harbour seal. Their build differs profoundly from that of other mammals.

Most striking is the transformation of their four limbs into powerful flippers. The body looks more spindle-shaped. It is covered with a thick layer of blubber and has a short coat. These animals are excellent swimmers and largely hunt for fish.

Surprisingly, their closest living relatives are bears, with which they share an ancestor. The oldest seal remains, which are about 25 million years old, were discovered in layers of rock. Seals can be found in all seas around the world, but most of them live in cold waters. Many live in coastal areas.

The size of seals varies considerably. Small species with a body length of 120 cm only weigh up to 70 kg, whilst large species weigh up to 3,500 kg with a body length of 6.50 m.

Although they live in water, they nevertheless frequent dry land in the mating season and to bask in the sun. But here they can only

move forward with difficulty, in a similar way to slow caterpillars. However, seals are usually fast and adept in the water. When seals are threatened, they produce rasping noises, which sound like barks or bleats.

California sea lion
Range: **west coast of North America**
Habitat: **coastal waters and islands**

Most seals are social animals and live in herds or in large extended families. A male (bull) can gather a harem of up to 40 females (cows) around him. After mating has taken place, a gestation period of 8–10 months follows, and then the female gives birth to a single pup and sometimes two, which grow fast.

Seals don't have many enemies. Their main predator is humans. In the past, a cruel seal cull took place every year. Therefore their numbers extensively declined. The teeth and the coat were especially prized, but also their oil and blubber.

Within the pinniped group of marine mammals, there is a distinction to be made between **walruses**, earless seals (true seals) and eared seals. Eared seals do actually have external ears (ear flaps), although they are only small ones. The 15 species in total can be further subdivided into sea lions and fur seals. Fur seals have a thicker undercoat than that of sea lions.

In contrast to eared seals, earless seals can no longer waddle along the ground, but can only crawl ('hump along') on their belly. They completely lack external ears (ear flaps) (but have ear canals behind the eyes). The harbour seal is a typical example of this group, which also includes the Baikal seal, grey seal, harp seal and bearded seal. The monk seal and elephant seal, as well as the crabeater seal, leopard seal, Weddell seal and hooded seal, are also classified as earless seals.

Harbour seal

The harbour seal (an earless seal) is found in the temperate and sub-arctic waters of the North Atlantic and the North Pacific. It has also been observed in the North Sea and the Baltic Sea.

Harbour seal

Range: **North Atlantic, North Pacific**
Habitat: **temperate, subarctic coastal waters**

Common seal (skeleton)

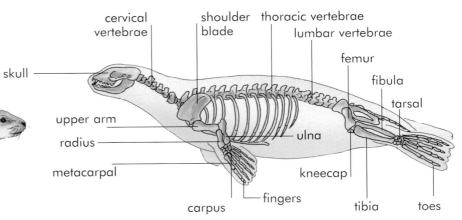

cervical vertebrae — shoulder blade — thoracic vertebrae — lumbar vertebrae — femur — fibula — tarsal — skull — upper arm — radius — ulna — metacarpal — kneecap — fingers — tibia — toes — carpus

This species of seal spends most of the day in the water. They only go ashore or onto the ice to bask in the sun or sleep.

The harbour seal is usually found in larger groups and its rasping bark can be heard even from a distance. Its head is relatively large with V-shaped nostrils. It has a stocky body and uses its short flippers, with the skin between them forming a web, to propel it along. Whilst the front flippers are flattened against its body when it swims, the hind flippers are stretched backwards and the soles of the flippers are turned towards

each other. By striking the flippers against each other, the water between them is displaced; that is to say, pushed backwards. Therefore the body is propelled forwards.

The smooth, flat coat is grey with darker spots. The animal is protected from the cold of the water by a thick layer of blubber. The females (cows) are smaller than the males (bulls), which grow up to 1.90 m in length.

Harbour seals eat fish, crustaceans and squid. They catch their prey at a depth of 50 m or more. Harbour seals usually only dive for 4–5 minutes, but can easily stay underwater for 20 minutes. The mouth is very similar to that of land predators. For every breath

they take, they open their V-shaped nostrils very wide. When these seals dive, the nostrils as well as the ear canals close.

The harbour seal is so skilful in the water yet moves so clumsily on land, where it can only move forwards with a 'hitching' action common to seals, which means that it draws up its rear end and then throws its whole body forwards. On land, it is easy prey for humans and polar bears.

Female harbour seals (cows) give birth to a single pup (rarely two) after a gestation period of 10–11 months.

Walrus

The walrus is a remarkable animal. It is found in the cold waters of the North Pole. Walrus males (bulls) reach 3.75 m in length and weigh 1,500 kg. The females (cows) are somewhat smaller.

The most prominent feature of this inelegant, huge animal is its tusks, which are directed downwards and have developed from the upper canine teeth. Tusks are also present in females, but they are much shorter and narrower.

Walruses do not feed on fish like

other members of the seal family (pinnipeds), but on molluscs. Walruses detect their prey with their highly sensitive, stiff bristles (vibrissae) when they are foraging at depths of up to 100 m. At the same time, they use their tusks to churn up the seabed. In addition, they eat crabs, starfish and also snails.

Walruses are found in large herds. During the mating season, they arrive at their traditional breeding ground. If the female's egg is fertilised, then delayed implantation occurs, which means that the egg does not implant in the mother's womb until 4–5 months

Walrus

Range: **Arctic waters and North Atlantic**
Habitat: **islands, coasts and pack ice**

later. Subsequently, after an actual gestation period of 11 months, she gives birth to a single pup and on rare occasions even two. Therefore the mother has a calf only every second year, which she then suckles for two years.

Walruses are important prey for the Inuit and the indigenous peoples of Siberia. A walrus provides a large quantity of meat, as well as oil for food and fuel. The skin can be used for covering boats. Tools and harpoon heads can be made from the ivory tusks, in addition to small figurines, which bring in a lot of money from tourists.

Because walruses were heavily exploited in previous centuries, their population was critically endangered for a long time.

Manatees

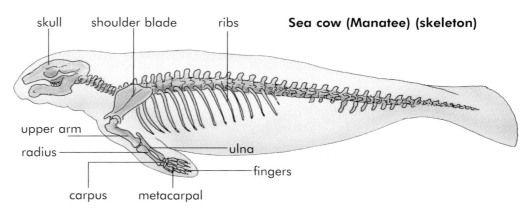

Manatee

Manatees are fully aquatic mammals, which are also called sirenians (manatees and dugongs). Even though they are similar to seals (pinnipeds), their nearest relatives are elephants.

Manatees have existed for some 50 million years. Today, four species survive that are found mainly in tropical and subtropical waters. They reach up to 4.5 m in length.

The manatee has sparse hairs

Sea cow (manatee)
Range: **South and Central America, West Africa**
Habitat: **tropical and subtropical waters**

Only the West Indian manatee lives mostly in the sea, or more precisely: in the warm coastal waters of the Atlantic Ocean off America. They can grow up to 3 m long and mainly eat at night. The two other manatee species live in the large river systems of the Amazon basin and West Africa.

Sea cow (Manatee) (skeleton)

skull | shoulder blade | ribs | upper arm | radius | ulna | carpus | metacarpal | fingers

scattered over its dumpy body. Short, stiff bristles (vibrissae) are located in the upper lip area of their thick fleshy snout. Their front limbs have transformed into flippers, whilst the rear limbs have completely disappeared. Their paddle-shaped tail is wider at the end.

Manatees can be found living alone or in groups. They feed exclusively on aquatic plants.

Manatee pups are born after a gestation period of 12–14 months. Depending on the species, it takes up to five years for them to reach sexual maturity.

Two families can be distinguished by the shape of their tail fin: the so-called **Fluke-Tailed Manatees** (dugongs) and the **Round-Tailed Manatees**. The **Dugong**, which is a member of the fluke-tailed manatee family, still survives today. It lives in the Indian Ocean, the Western Pacific and the Red Sea. This animal can grow up to 3.2 m long. The males of this family have a pair of short tusks, which have developed from the incisors. **Steller's Sea Cow**, which also belonged to this group and weighed up to 4,000 kg, has become extinct.

Manatees (round-tailed sea cows) reach a length of 4.5 m. They live in the rivers and seas of eastern Central America and eastern South America, as well as in West Africa. Manatees lack tusks. They only have molars ('marching molars'), which fall out according to wear and tear, and are then constantly replaced.

Manatee populations have dramatically declined in many areas, due to fishing, shipping, environmental pollution and hunting.

INDEX